Effective Teaching of Science

A REVIEW OF RESEARCH

Wynne Harlen

The Scottish Council for Research in Education

SCRE Publication 142
Using Research Series 21

Series editors: Wynne Harlen
                  Rosemary Wake

Published 1999

ISBN 1 86003 048 3

The views expressed are those of the author and should not be taken as being those of the Scottish Council for Research in Education or the Scottish Office Education and Industry Department.

Cover photograph: Douglas Corrance

Design and typesetting by SCRE Information Services.

Printed and bound in Great Britain for the Scottish Council for Research in Education, 15 St John Street, Edinburgh EH8 8JR, by Bell & Bain, 303 Burnfield Road, Thornliebank, Glasgow G46 7UQ.

Contents

Abbreviations

AAP   Assessment of Achievement Programme. This is Scotland's national monitoring programme which has since the early 1980s conducted regular surveys of pupil achievement in English, mathematics and science in Scottish schools, using a light sample of pupils aged 8/9, 11/12 and 13/14.

APU   Assessment of Performance Unit. This was the national monitoring programme of England, Wales and Northern Ireland from 1977 to 1987.

BSCS   Biological Science Curriculum Study. A major curriculum development project of the 1950s and 1960s in the US.

CASE   Cognitive Acceleration through Science Education.

ICT   Information and Communications Technology (In the US: Information and Computer Technology).

IEA/TIMSS   The International Association for the Evaluation of Educational Achievement's most recent survey, the Third International Mathematics and Science Study.

MARS   Model-based Analysis and Reasoning in Science.

NAEP   National Assessment of Educational Performance.

OECD   Organisation for Economic Co-operation and Development.

PCAST   President's Committee of Advisors on Science and Technology.

PSSC   Physical Science Study Committee, which was responsible for major change in the physics curriculum beginning in the late 1950s in the US.

PSTS   Primary School Teachers and Science project.

SCRE   The Scottish Council for Research in Education.

SOEID   Scottish Office Education and Industry Department.

SOLSN   Science On-line Support Network.

1

Introduction

Background

Concern has been widely expressed about the appropriateness and effectiveness of science education for meeting the needs of future citizens. Science education in school has to fulfil two roles: to prepare future scientists and technologists and to provide all citizens with sufficient knowledge and understanding to enable them to make sensible decisions about science-related issues that affect all our lives. The first of these has had a strong influence on school science in the past but it is now generally agreed that in the future far more attention should be given to the second role. In considering how science education can best meet new as well as existing aims, it is useful to review current practice and to take advantage of the considerable developments in the past two decades, for example, in understanding of learning in science and in computer technology.

These issues formed the wider background to this study, although the specific impetus for it was as a contribution to a review of science teaching in upper primary and lower secondary schools by HM Inspectors of Schools in Scotland, requested by the Scottish Office. The aim of the study was 'to examine UK and international research carried out on primary and secondary school science teaching to identify approaches and techniques which have proved effective in raising standards'. It was conducted in the wake of findings from national and international surveys of student achievement that showed deficiencies in Scottish pupils' performance particularly at the end of the first two years of secondary school and to some extent at the end of primary school. What has been revealed about effective teaching and learning through the review has, however, relevance beyond the context of science in Scottish schools.

Evidence from national surveys

A feature of Scottish education is the continued operation of the Assessment of Achievement Programme (AAP), which was instituted in 1984. Since 1987 the AAP has surveyed achievement in English, mathematics and science in a three-year cycle. The fourth survey of science of the AAP, conducted in 1996, was the first in which the findings were analysed in relation to the targets of the 5–14 Curriculum Guidelines. The results of this analysis suggested that 8/9-year-olds (P4) were showing the level of performance expected in the guidelines and that 11/12 year-olds (P7) were close to expectations. This was considered acceptable, given that the implementation of the guidelines for science was at an early stage in about half of primary schools (Malcolm and Schlapp, 1997). However at the age of 13/14, in S4, at the end of two years of secondary school in which science was taught in all schools, performance fell short of expectations.

Comparisons across the last three AAP science surveys (1990, 1993 and 1996) showed that for written tasks there had been a rise in performance of P4 pupils, the performance of P7 pupils had remained steady and that performance of S2 pupils had fallen. It is perhaps worthy of note that at P4 the girls' performance had risen more than the boys', at P7 there was no difference, and at S2 there was a slightly larger decline in score of boys than of girls over the years (SOEID, 1998).

International surveys

Scotland has taken part in major international surveys conducted by the International Association for the Evaluation of Educational Achievement (IEA) and the International Assessment of Educational Progress (IAEP). The results of the Third International Mathematics and Science Study (TIMSS) carried out by the IEA in the school year 1994/95 enabled Scottish pupils' performance to be compared with that of similar pupils in other countries. The principal findings show up particularly clearly when only OECD countries are considered for comparison (OECD, 1997). For Population 1 (age 9/10) Scottish pupils' performance was not significantly different from the OECD international average, whilst for Population 2 (13/14) the Scottish average was significantly below this international average. The relatively small advance in performance between these ages compared with other countries is shown in Figure 1, where Scotland is among the five lowest countries in terms of advance and only one of two (with Canada) where this small advance cannot be explained in terms of higher achievement at the lower age group.

Figure 1: *Mean science achievement at ages 9/10 and 13/14 (1995) (Source OECD 1997 p305)*

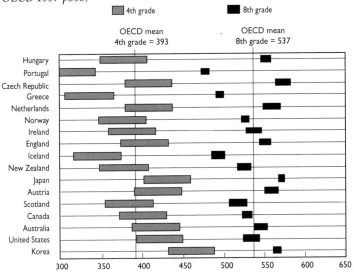

Note: Countries are ranked in descending order of difference in means between 4th and 8th grades.

A further point of interest is that the spread of scores in Scotland, as measured by the difference between the scores, at the lower age group was among the four highest. This wide range suggests a variation of achievement within classes and schools which may be due to uneven learning opportunities at the primary level. As Figure 1 suggests (in the length of the bar for the 8th grade) this difference is less at the upper age level, perhaps due to more uniform experiences in science lessons, but it is still among the largest compared with other OECD countries.

Gender differences in Scotland were small and favouring boys at age 9/10; the boys' advantage was greater at age 13/14.

Data concerning the association of attitudes with performance were given only for mathematics. For age 13/14 students in all countries, students with positive attitudes towards mathematics had higher levels of performance than others, but across countries the highest performing countries were not those showing the most positive attitudes.

The findings of these major national and international surveys support each other in pointing to some concern about the science education of pupils in Scotland in the first two years of secondary school and, since these build on the foundation laid earlier, that at the top of the primary school. Although there has been a steady rise in both uptake and in performance in science subjects in the Standard Grade examinations at the age of 16 throughout the 1980s and early 1990s (Harlen, 1995), the continuation of this into the next century is unlikely to be assured unless the decline in performance lower down in the secondary school can be reversed. The purpose of the review was, therefore, to identify clues from research that might indicate where change, and what change, could be helpful.

The structure of the review

Teaching science is multifaceted; there is no single variable which can be changed without affecting other aspects or even a collection of variables which can be manipulated as a whole in the expectation of improving achievement. Research studies have each focused on one or two aspects, leaving the combined effect of changes in several aspects as outcomes which can only be inferred. The main section of this review considers research into the following aspects:

- the role of practical work
- the use of computers
- approaches to constructivism
- cognitive acceleration
- assessment
- planning, questioning and using language
- the curriculum
- teachers' understanding of science.

In the final section there is an attempt to summarise and bring together, as far as possible, the conclusions that can be drawn from combining findings from studies of the different aspects.

Criteria for selection of studies

A selection had to be made from the vast quantity of research on science education. The main criteria used were the following:

- some comparison was made between two or more groups differing in experiences relating to one of the above aspects of science education
- the studies involved upper primary or lower secondary school pupils or older pupils where the findings could be applied to other age groups or where they illuminated reasons for approaches being effective at particular stages
- comparisons were made in terms of achievement in science or outcomes related to achievement
- the innovation was sustainable in normal classrooms and not just in specially controlled and favourable conditions.

In addition, reference is made to changes in teaching which have been proposed and arise from closely observed practice but which have not been rigorously tested for their effectiveness in comparison with traditional methods.

2

The Role of Practical Work

Joan Solomon began her book on *Teaching Children in the Laboratory* (1980) with the words:

> Science teaching must take place in the laboratory; about that at least there is no controversy. Science simply belongs there as naturally as cooking belongs in the kitchen and gardening in the garden. (p13)

She traced this conviction back to the influence of H E Armstrong at the beginning of the century and the later period of great expansion and enthusiasm for science education which created, and was sustained by, the science projects of the 1960s. These included the Nuffield projects in junior and secondary schools in the UK and the PSSC, BSCS and CHEM study in the US.

Writing her book at the end of the 1970s, Solomon recognised that there were many questions about how to conduct practical work, but did not question the value of practical work itself. However just what this value was had been investigated by a study of practical work in secondary schools by Kerr (1963). Kerr asked science teachers to rank the possible aims of practical work and found considerable agreement in that, for the first two years of the secondary school (ages 11 and 12), the most important aims were concerned with interest in science, while for the 13–15 year-olds the main aims were concerned with promoting scientific methods and ways of thinking. Later studies (eg Beatty and Woolnough, 1982) found little change in teachers' priorities although they did detect a shift favouring the development of practical skills rather than the development of understanding. It is interesting that at the sixth-form level both Gould (1978) and Gayford (1988) found the greatest emphasis was on 'promoting accurate observation' and the least on 'developing problem-solving skills'.

Doubts as to the value of practical work in secondary schools began to emerge in the 1980s, partly in acknowledgement that poor facilities often militated against it, but also, as Hofstein and Lunetta (1982) pointed out:

> Few teachers in secondary schools are competent to use the laboratory effectively...
>
> Too much emphasis on laboratory activities leads to a narrow conception of science...
>
> Too many experiments performed in school are trivial...
>
> Laboratory work in schools is often remote from, and unrelated to, the capabilities and interests of the children.
>
> (Quoted by Hodson, 1993, p87)

Claims for practical work

In a seminal review of research into practical work in school science, Hodson (1993) considers the evidence supporting the popular claims made about practical work: that it served to motivate, to teach skills, to enhance conceptual learning, to give insight into the scientific method and, to develop scientific attitudes such as open-mindedness, objectivity and willingness to suspend judgement. The following sections summarise his conclusions in relation to each of these goals.

Motivation

There is no evidence that increasing the amount of practical work increases pupils' interest and motivation in relation to science. Gardner and Gauld (1990) reported mixed reactions to laboratory work and, in common with other researchers, found that what students like about practical work is not related to what they learn:

> Often it is the opportunity to engage in the variety of active learning methods, to interact more freely with the teacher and with other children, and to pace the work as it suits them, that appeals, rather than the opportunity to conduct bench work investigations *per se*. (p91)

Hodson's own work (1990) in New Zealand found 57% of 13 to 16-year-olds liking practical work but 40% indicating less motivation when they didn't know what they were doing or when things went wrong. He concluded from this and a variety of other studies that students value practical work when:

- it provides a cognitive challenge
- it has a clear purpose and 'works'
- it gives them sufficient control and independence.

The kind of practical work in which many pupils are engaged changes markedly in moving from primary to secondary school. In the former it may be fairly unstructured and decided at least to some extent by the pupils; in the secondary school it may be more teacher-directed and involve following instructions. The laboratory itself, for many, may be seen as an environment with little relevance to everyday life. When the work in it does not give them a sense of achievement, the combination of irrelevance and frustration can be deterring rather than motivating.

Development of skills

Hodson (1993) points to two kinds of skills in relation to the arguments which have been put forward for the value of practical work. The first concerns the acquisition of generalisable skills which may be of value outside the laboratory and the second concerns those skills required by future scientists. He describes the arguments for the first of these as 'bordering on the absurd' since:

> It is difficult to see, for example, in what sense the ability to use a pipette and burette successfully, in volumetric analysis, is transferable to a laboratory context in which an oscilloscope or microscope is to be employed or a dogfish dissected. It is even more difficult to see how such a skill can be transferred to a non-laboratory situation in everyday life. (p93)

There is also evidence from the Assessment of Performance Unit (APU) surveys that only a minority of pupils can carry out standard procedures or use standard laboratory equipment correctly at the age of 15 (APU, 1986). As to the second set of skills, Hodson suggests that it is ethically dubious and 'hopelessly over-ambitious' to attempt to develop research skills in all pupils regardless of whether they will study science to a higher level.

Given these arguments and the evidence that inadequate skill can mean that time is wasted in the laboratory and constitute an obstacle to learning, Hodson concludes that:

- only those skills should be taught that are of value in pursuit of other learning and, when this is the case, we should ensure that those skills are developed to a satisfactory level of competence
- when successful engagement in an experiment requires a skill that children will not need again... alternatives should be found such as pre-assembly of apparatus, teacher demonstration, computer simulation, etc. (p94)

Conceptual learning

The notion that practical work aids understanding underpinned the approaches of the Nuffield Science Projects in the 1960s. The (supposedly) Chinese proverb 'I hear and I forget, I see and I remember, I do and I understand' was quoted as embodying the arguments in support of practical work. However the studies reviewed by Hodson provide no evidence for the superiority of practical work over other teaching methods in developing scientific knowledge. On balance the evidence has tended to point in the direction of practical work being less successful in this than other methods. But it is necessary to be cautious in drawing any conclusions since there are considerable difficulties in interpreting the data due to shortcomings in the research methodology of studies which purport to compare methods of teaching. These shortcomings include small group size, inadequate control of variables, the impact of differences between teachers, and the use of inappropriate measures of gain in knowledge and understanding. There is also a range of interpretations of 'practical work' with significantly different emphasis given to experimental design, observation and measurement, handling equipment, interpretation of results and so on, so that it is difficult to know exactly what is the independent variable in these studies.

A study of the effect of an experiment-based physical science programme on students in grades 4 to 8 in the US was carried out by Reynolds (1991). He found no effect on cognitive outcomes and a small effect on science process skills but only for the students of motivated teachers.

Insight into the scientific method

Findings from research on the effect of practical work on students' understanding of the nature of scientific enquiry are as negative as those for conceptual understanding – and for much the same methodological reasons. Hodson cites several studies which lead to the conclusion that:

> individual practical work often seems to be counter-productive, leading to a somewhat distorted and incoherent understanding of scientific methodology. (p95)

Scientific attitudes

The concern is with the attitudes which are conventionally described as 'scientific' – open-mindedness, willingness to consider evidence, for example – rather than 'attitudes to science' (Gauld and Hukins, 1980). These attitudes appear frequently in the goals of science education at both primary and secondary levels often on the assumption that they are characteristics of scientists and underlie scientific discoveries. This view has been challenged by sociological studies of individual scientists and also of particular discoveries. For example Holton's (1978) study of Millikan's notebooks at the time when Millikan was carrying out the oil-drop experiment – which was central in deciding the issue of whether electric charge existed only as multiples of an elementary charge or could take any value – showed evidence that data were omitted which did not support his hypothesis. Gauld, from a study of the Millikan case and other examples concludes that scientists respond to experimental data with a variety of strategies which enable them to retain their theories in the face of discrepant evidence, just as learners in school are known to do. Thus the arguments for pursuing these attitudes because they characterise successful scientists have been undermined.

Even if it can be argued that these attitudes are desirable for pursuing scientific enquiries, the evidence from the type of practical work found in much secondary science – where what seems important is getting the right answer – would suggest that they are unlikely to be fostered. Thus the conclusions reached by Gardner and Gauld (1990) seem little more than common sense, in that merely being in the laboratory and doing laboratory work do not, by themselves, foster scientific attitudes. What is crucial, they emphasised, is the quality of the experiences that students have there.

Shortcomings of practical work

Several studies have thrown light on possible reasons for practical work not living up to the claims made for it.

The meaning of 'on-task'

Practical work is generally carried out in groups and thus its impact on learning is influenced by the individuals in the group and their interactions. A close study of students' talk in groups during individual and group activities was carried out by Alton-Lee, Nuthall and Patrick (1993) in the *Understanding Learning and Teaching Project* in New Zealand. The part of their fascinating findings which is relevant here concerns 'off-task' and 'on-task' behaviour recorded verbatim using individual radio microphones for each student. They found relatively little talk that was unrelated to the task in hand. However, much of the on-task talk was preoccupied with the organisation of the task and details such as printing headings, using colours in drawings. The authors reported:

> From our detailed records of children's experience of curriculum in the classrooms we studied, it is clear that off-task behaviour played a relatively minor role in inhibiting learning, as compared with on-task behaviour that did not involve engagement with curriculum concepts. (p58)

This failure to get to grips with the purpose of the activity rather than being concerned with the procedures of carrying out instructions is not always visible to the teacher and, indeed, as Alton-Lee *et al* showed, not always clear to the observer who does not have access to the students' talk. Similar findings emerge from close study of students working with interactive learning environments (Plowman, 1997) and video-discs. Baird and Mitchell (1986) reported several instances of different perceptions of a task as seen by the pupils and the teacher which lead to attention being given to parts of the task not specifically related to the phenomena being studied, such as the details of a drawing or precise spelling when making notes.

Nuthall and Alton-Lee (1992) have suggested that students learn by making links with previous experience, elaborating and evaluating their developing concepts and developing meta-cognitive awareness. From their study Alton-Lee *et al* found that students are more likely to do these things following questions and cues from the teacher than during group working.

Signal to noise

Several studies have revealed the complexity of tasks that pupils are faced with in experimental work. Often this includes reading instructions, manipulating equipment (which may be more complicated than necessary for the work in hand and may not function correctly), making measurements, recording, negotiating with members of a group – all before there is any chance of arriving at a result which impacts on their learning. Thus it is not surprising that much of their time, as reported above, is spent on task-related activity but does not relate to the curriculum purpose of the work. In other words, there is too much 'noise' in the system. Johnstone and Wham (1982) recognised this in chemistry practical work and observed that pupils may as a result adopt one of several strategies for dealing with the situation:

- Adopt a 'recipe approach', following the steps in the instruction mechanically
- Focus on one aspect of the experiment, to the virtual exclusion of everything else
- Exhibit random behaviour in which they are 'very busy getting nowhere'
- Look around them in order to copy what others are doing
- Become 'helpers' or assistants to a group organised and run by others.

To counter these problems, Johnstone and Letton (1990) advocate greater care in preparing students and in designing experiments and the use of a problem-solving approach. Woolnough (1997) goes further, after first criticising the kind of practical work 'which is designed to enable students to discover or verify some scientific theory, often using complicated apparatus and occupying a considerable amount of most science lessons...' (p70) for the amount of 'distracting clutter' that clouds the underlying purpose and 'eliminates any possibility of individual planning and problem-solving'. He proposes that for developing understanding it would be better to rely on demonstration, exposition and discussion, reserving practical work by pupils for investigations which they have helped to devise and which 'give a genuine experience of doing science'.

Knowing what is significant

Several researchers (eg Driver and Bell, 1986; White, 1991; Gunstone, 1991) have shown that it entirely possible for students to misinterpret what they find in practical work because their attention is focused by their own misconceptions. Because they have a different idea of what is happening they observe what is consistent with their idea rather than what they were 'expected' to observe. Consequently they may emerge with their misconceptions confirmed rather than challenged. Hodson suggests that this arises because teachers have not involved students in devising the experiments and have assumed that the students' ability to observe is unaffected by any existing ideas. Moreover there is a hangover from the confusion of pupil-centred approaches with 'outdated inductivist ideas about the nature of scientific inquiry' (Hodson, 1993).

Appropriate practical work

Krishner (1992) made an important contribution to reflecting on the appropriate role for practical work in science education by pointing out that because experimentation is central to science it is not necessarily central to science education. Hodson (1992a) helped to clarify the role of practical work by making a distinction between *learning science, learning about science* and *doing science.*

Learning science

Learning science is about making sense of the world around and this means experiencing the phenomena that are to be explained:

> It isn't enough to read about magnesium burning with a brilliant white flame or about light bending as it passes through a prism. Students need to experience these things at first hand and to handle objects and organisms for themselves in order to build up a stock of personal experience. (p110)

Practical work also has a role in learning science through enabling pupils to test, rethink and reconstruct their ideas. (There is more discussion of this in the chapter on constructivism.) The point here is that practical work is one way of assisting the crucial process of enabling pupils to explore their own and others' ideas. But it is only one way and there are others such as concept mapping, discussion and debate, using computer programs, writing, role-play, field work and library-based research. Osborne (1997) has listed several alternatives to practical work which can be used to develop conceptual understanding. These include small-group work discussing misconceptions about particular instances, disentangling jumbled sentences and identifying errors in a false concept map. Laboratory work has a role here but only when pupils are consciously involved in designing the work and it has a meaning for them.

Only when ideas different from their own are seen by pupils to be more fruitful than their own in explaining phenomena and in making predictions, will they be prepared to adopt them. As has often been pointed out, many scientific ideas are counter-intuitive and on the surface make less sense than pupils' own ideas. Thus it takes time for pupils to change their ideas and, as Gunstone and Champagne (1990) suggest, more class time should be spent on manipulating ideas and less on manipulating apparatus.

Learning about science

Learning about science, as has been pointed out by Tamir (1985), is often implicit rather than explicit. It is part of a 'hidden curriculum' of science education, conveyed through the language and methods used in the laboratory. Studies have shown that there is a strong influence of the teacher and of the particular curriculum on children's views about science. Benson (1986) found considerable consistency in the views of children within a class and considerable differences between classes. This was ascribed to the choice of activities and class materials made by the teacher which in turn reflect his/her philosophical stance in relation to science. The influence of classroom materials was demonstrated by Carey *et al* (1989) who showed that 12-year-old children's understanding of how scientific knowledge is constructed was strongly influenced by a teaching unit on the nature of science. However Hodson (1993) suggested that there was evidence that teachers changed their approach when teaching classes of different ability, 'Thus, teachers who might adopt a hypothetical-deductive approach with high ability children may adopt an inductivist stance with those they consider to be less able' (p113).

If pupils are to learn about science there needs to be more explicit discussion of the models of science which have been embraced in recent history. The different relationships between theory and experiment in these models are best brought together, according to Hodson (1993), 'by encouraging students to regard theory and experiments as having an inter-dependent and interactive relationship; experiments assist theory-building; theory, in turn, determines the kind of experiments that can and should be carried out' (p115). While providing for pupils to carry out their own investigations can be helpful in achieving this understanding, a number of other activities have an important role. These include historical case-studies, simulations and dramatic reconstructions (Solomon *et al*, 1992), materials focusing on the nature of science (Carey *et al*, 1989; Solomon *et al*, 1992), discussion of topics where theoretical explanations are controversial (Millar, 1989) and thought experiments (Adams, 1991).

Doing science

There is no alternative to pupils undertaking some scientific activity for themselves if doing science is a valued part of science education. Although this will often mean direct manipulation of equipment, relevant experience can be obtained through computer-based activities such as the interrogation of data-bases. Hodson (1993) claims that scientists gain a double benefit from engaging in scientific inquiry – an increase in their understanding of scientific activity and in their capacity to do it successfully. It follows that:

> If scientists enhance their professional expertise through practice, it is reasonable to suppose that students will learn to do science (and learn to do it *better*) by doing science – simple investigations at first, probably chosen from a well-tried list of 'successful' investigations designed and developed by the teachers, but whole investigations nonetheless. (p120). (Emphasis in the original)

Hodson (1992a) insists that doing science is a holistic activity: 'in carrying out investigations, scientists refine their approach to the problem, develop greater understanding of it and devise more appropriate and productive ways of proceeding all at the same time' (p72). Therefore it essential for achieving the ability to do science that pupils undertake whole investigations, as individuals or in groups, taking a considerable degree of control of the direction the work takes. Younger and less-experienced pupils need to begin with simple and well-defined investigations, moving to those where they have more control as their confidence grows. Often science clubs out of normal school time provide this experience successfully, being free from the constraints of class time and formal teacher-pupil relationships.

Group work or demonstration?

In some cases the choice between demonstration or benchwork by pupils is decided by the type of equipment that is needed. In other cases, where there is a real choice, and either could achieve the purpose of the work, the teacher's style is an important determinant. The work of Garnett and Tobin (1988) is relevant in this context although it was reported in relation to effectiveness in teaching for understanding ('learning science' in the sense used above). Garnett and Tobin's study was part of a larger investigation of exemplary practice in teaching science and mathematics carried out in Western Australia (Tobin and Fraser, 1987).

Two teachers were selected for close study having been identified by State Education Department personnel and by tertiary science educators as outstanding teachers of chemistry. Each teacher was observed by a researcher for 20 lessons and six pupils across the ability range were interviewed to find their perceptions of the teacher's role and of how learning and teaching were taking place. In-depth interviews were also held with each teacher as well as more frequent discussions after each lesson. The teachers, both male, had strikingly contrasting styles of teaching yet both were judged to be effective in bringing about learning with understanding.

One teacher believed that the students would achieve the high level of understanding that he was aiming for by developing independence and accepting responsibility for their learning. He allocated a good proportion of class time to individual or group work, planning it with the students at the beginning of each lesson and supervising it by constantly moving round the room, interacting with students, asking probing questions and maintaining a high level of engagement with the task. The group or individual tasks included using books and audio-visual aids as well as practical work. There was little use of demonstration.

The other teacher believed that he had a direct and crucial part to play in explaining new material to students. He spent more time in whole class teaching and used this to link new material to previous learning, explaining the subject matter clearly with the help of demonstrations. There was also some laboratory work carried out by the students which was mainly to give them first-hand experience so that they could better understand the concepts introduced to them directly by the teacher.

The students' reactions to both teachers were positive and in both classes they appreciated the opportunities to ask questions and felt they had sympathetic help from their teachers. Although these teachers used practical work in two very different ways, in both cases it was integrated into a style of teaching which was designed to develop understanding. What they had in common is taken up later (in Chapter 7), but the evidence from this study suggests that what is important is not whether demonstration or bench work is used but whether either is used effectively so as to achieve the purpose of the teaching.

Many attempts have been made to compare directly the impact on achievement of small-group practical work and demonstrations but none of those in the last 20 years has found any significant difference. For example, Garrett and Roberts (1982) studied over 300 11 to 12-year-olds in six schools as they were exposed to small-group work and demonstration by the same teachers. There was an attempt by the teachers to keep to the same 'guided discovery' approach in both types of practical exposure. There were no overall significant differences and no difference between boys and girls. The researchers reported that, '…the most consistent indicators were that teachers and materials were more important factors in causing any differences than were the teaching tactics' (p136). These authors, as part of an extensive review of demonstration versus small group practical work, were heavily critical of the design of the studies and suggested that, '… as long as researchers look for gross overall changes, or differences, in pupil outcomes, then simple changes in teaching tactics will not produce overall measurable results.' (p137)

Some conclusions about practical work

- Practical work should be seen as a means to various ends and not as an end in itself.

- The learning that is intended from a particular piece of practical work should be clear and it should to be tailored in order that it can serve that purpose effectively.

- Both teachers and pupils need to be aware of the purpose of the practical work in a particular case and prepare for it and follow it up in relation to the specific purpose.

- There are three main purposes for practical work which have emerged from this review:
  - Providing first-hand experience, so that pupils can 'see it for themselves' and in some cases do it themselves, although this purpose is often best served by a good demonstration or a field trip rather than 'hands on' practical work.
  - Testing ideas by making predictions, setting up a valid test, collecting reliable evidence and relating what is found to the original idea. This practical work should be theory-based.
  - Experience of 'doing science' through carrying out an investigation which has a degree of open-endedness.

3

Using Computers

Programs for computer-assisted instruction (CAI) have been developed since the 1960s to provide individually-paced tutoring in many areas of the curriculum. In traditional CAI, feedback to the student is provided about their answers to questions interspersed in the teaching material. In some programs branches and loops are used to tailor routes through the material in response to the kind of answer given to the questions. More sophisticated programs have the capability of identifying types of error or misunderstanding and of matching further input to them. In practice, however, there is a limit to the application of these programs beyond, for example, simple arithmetic and other basic skills.

Over the years, considerable research effort has been devoted to evaluating the impact of these types of program and meta-analyses of many studies have been carried out by Bangert-Drowns *et al* (1985) and Kulik and Kulik (1990). Their results follow the pattern of other meta-analyses of the effectiveness of CAI in showing a significant effect on achievement in test scores, particularly for students of low-socio-economic status, low-achievers and students with special educational needs. However, many of the early studies have been criticised for methodological flaws and their relevance to more recent practice, using more powerful, networked computers has been questioned.

In relation to science education, recent developments use computers as part of a more varied educational experience rather than as a replacement for classroom and laboratory work. Currently (that is, in the late 1990s) the main applications are word-processing, data-logging, graphing, simulations, modelling, analysing data using databases and spreadsheets and accessing information through the Internet. Some of these have been researched in more depth than others.

Word-processing

Word-processing in science provides all the benefits common to its use in other areas of the curriculum. The particular advantages for science seem to arise when children begin to use word-processing as routine throughout practical work and not just to produce a report at the end. Clough (1987), a primary headteacher, observed the impact of the introduction of word-processing on primary pupils and noted that:

> ...when the writing up stage is seen as an integral part of the scientific process it can be used to develop an awareness in children of the importance of attention to detail and to promote a more thorough understanding of what they are doing. (p5)

Clough observed changes following the introduction of word-processing which went beyond the quality of the written output, including attention to detail, improved note-taking during practical work and increased motivation, particularly of less able pupils.

Data-logging

Research on data-logging leads to several conclusions with implications for the role of practical work in science. The findings of Newton (1997) although derived from observations of pupils who were new to data-logging, reflected those of several other studies (eg Rogers and Wild, 1996). Newton observed and tape-recorded the conversations of pupils in the first two years of a secondary school in England. The pupils' investigation involved recording the temperature of gases in two plastic drinks bottles, one containing air and one containing air enriched with carbon dioxide, as they were heated by a 100 watt lamp. They used temperature sensors connected to LogIT data-loggers and computers (Acorn Pocket Books) with appropriate software. The recordings showed that a large part of the students' talk during data-logging was concerned with how to set up and operate the equipment. Newton suggested that this may have been a result of the novelty of the equipment to the pupils and indeed as a general finding (see the later section on interactive multimedia) it may be an artefact of the introduction of new technology that will disappear when it becomes a more routine part of pupils' work.

The data-logging process has the advantage that pupils see the data being recorded from moment to moment in real time and their attention can be given to the trends and patterns as they appear. This is in contrast with conventional practical work, where the focus of attention is the individual data point. However, watching lines being created on graphs on the screen can be as unproductive, and indeed boring, as repetitive collecting of readings directly from instruments. Several of the pupils in Newton's study reported not enjoying, 'watching the lines going up or down or staying the same'. The potential advantages of data-logging over conventional practical work are realised only when the teacher mediates the process of making sense of the data as it appears on the screen. The recordings of pupils' talk showed that the pupils' interpretations were more closely related to the experiment (and not just seen as a 'race' between two lines on the screen) when the teacher encouraged them to articulate the meaning of the lines on the graph and to make predictions of the possible effects of changes in the experiment.

One of the obvious advantages of data-logging is that it saves time. Pupils don't have to be watching the screen as data are recorded; indeed this can happen when they are not present. For example, an activity for primary pupils is to record the level of light over a full 24 hours in order to identify the exact time of sunrise and sunset (Sensor! 1998) or, for older pupils, the levels of light, temperature and dissolved oxygen in an aquarium (Rogers, 1997). Opportunities to extend primary pupils' experience are particularly rich, given that the use of conventional measuring instruments with sufficient accuracy to be useful in some contexts is not feasible.

Graphing

A direct comparison of three approaches to data collection and graphing was conducted by Barton (1997) using samples of pupils from two comprehensive schools in three ability bands aged 12/13 and 14/15. The curriculum area chosen for the study was the measurement of the electrical characteristics of circuit components such as resistors, bulbs and diodes. The three approaches were computer-aided practical work, conventional practical work and a non-practical task giving equivalent information. Comparisons were made in terms of the time spent on different activities and an analysis of the activities using a video-recording of each session. It is interesting that the pupils' reactions towards the non-practical activity were not negative. Barton reported:

> Pupils in both year groups and in all three ability bands enjoyed the activity and were the most outspoken about the drawbacks of practical work. They liked the ability to get more done using the non-practical approach and several commented on the way they tended to get confused and distracted by conventional practical work, particularly one involving wires. (p57)

Comparing computer-aided and manual plotting of graphs, Barton found, as might be expected, that manual plotting presented greater difficulty to most pupils, particularly the younger and least able: only the more able older pupils could complete the necessary graph unaided and even then with several errors. The problems presented by graphing meant that pupils were not questioning their data as they recorded it, nor identifying any emerging relationships between the variables being plotted. The attention of the pupils using the computer, by contrast, was not taken by the individual data points but much more by the trends in the data. There was a further difference between the groups in the matter of realising that in some cases the points would not fit a straight line, which was the first assumption of all the pupils. Those using the computer had the advantage of seeing the graph produced for them and this led them to attempt some interpretation of the different shapes of the lines far more quickly than the non-computer group. Also significant was a time difference, since the manual graphing pupils spent between two and four times longer than those using the computer, the difference being greater for the younger pupils.

Barton investigated the effect of the different experience on the ability of three groups to interpret graphs and to use them to make predictions. He summarised his findings as follows:

- For year 10 pupils (14/15-year-olds) of average ability and above, there were no major differences in pupils' ability to interpret graphical data using the different methods.
- Where difference did occur, the extra materials covered by the computer groups resulted in their interpretations containing more detail.

- Handling equipment didn't seem to make any difference to pupils' ability to interpret the graphs.

- Manual plotting tended to emphasise individual data items rather than the continuous nature of the relationship between the variables.

- Describing graphs is much more effective where a second graph is present.

- No advantages were observed associated with manual graph plotting.

Simulations

Scaife and Wellington (1993) list various types of computer simulation, from direct copies of existing laboratory activities, through simulations of industrial processes, to simulations based on constructs such as ideal gases and frictionless surfaces and ones based on models or theories. They also list the advantages and disadvantages of computer simulations. Advantages relate to costs such as reducing expenditure on consumables and multiple sets of equipment, time, safety, motivation of pupils, control by pupils and management problems (many fewer than with the distribution and collection of equipment). At the same time, the disadvantages relate to the image of reality that the simulations can give. On this point Scaife and Wellington (1993, p46) mention in particular:

- Simulations give pupils the impression that variables in physical processes can be easily, equally and independently controlled.

- Users can only manipulate the factors and variables that are built into the model; they cannot tamper with the model itself.

- Any model is an idealisation of reality and ignores certain features in order to concentrate on others. This can be misleading and represent a caricature of reality rather than a representation of it.

- Pupils are almost certain to confound the programmer's reality with reality itself.

- These dangers are even greater when the simulation is of a model which is itself an idealisation of reality.

The simulation of an everyday phenomenon was used in an investigation by Lewis *et al* (1993). They developed what they described as 'a computer-based curriculum' to encourage students' deeper learning of thermodynamics. Their hypothesis was that:

an opportunity to actively investigate naturally occurring problems using computer simulations, combined with activities that encouraged students to directly consider their prior experiences, would encourage students to construct a more robust view of thermodynamics. (p46)

Their reformulated curriculum on thermodynamics (for 8th grade students, aged 12 to 14) had three main components: practical data-collection integrated with computer simulation of the same everyday phenomena (eg the cooling of hot potatoes or cold drinks warming up); using the computer simulation for prediction and reflection and a computer notebook to record the prediction and results; and a model for heat flow introduced, not by computer, but during classroom discussions. The students worked in fours (dictated by the number of computers with enough memory) and within the groups each member was assigned an individual role at any one time. Five classes used the computer-based program for a semester and their performance on tests was compared to that of a similar group who studied the regular curriculum on thermodynamics in the previous semester. The results showed that the students using the computer had increased their performance over previous students in explaining naturally occurring phenomena and in drawing cooling curves. Their performance in explaining heat and temperature graphs correctly was similar to that of the previous students, which was taken as a positive outcome since the computer-based work had given less coverage to relevant variables. Evidence of several kinds supported the view that there was 'an increase in students' integrated understanding'. Probable reasons for this proposed by the authors were: the greater number of simulated experiments that students could carry out on the computer compared with real-life experiments; the inclusion of real-world simulated phenomena; the concrete nature of the experiments; and the laboratory notebook which facilitated the re-use of ideas. However the researchers' expectations were not met in several other respects:

- students often did not understand that they should be reflecting upon what they found

- the students had difficulty knowing what they should be giving attention to
- they were not very good at testing their own hypotheses and 'debugging their own knowledge'
- they often extended the interpretation of their results so as to confirm their own ideas
- there was little evidence of the students' use of the model of heat flow that was offered.

Modelling

Modelling differs in intent from simulation, although in some cases the distinction is blurred. In modelling, pupils are able to work out for themselves how variables relate to each other, whereas in simulations they are looking at the outcomes of manipulating the model built into the program. Ogborn (1990) has given a general discussion of the role of modelling in science education. Scaife and Wellington (1993) discuss the role of the computer in modelling, which they suggest should be to take on the 'inauthentic labour' of programming, calculating and presentation, leaving 'the user to focus on the intellectually creative task of devising and exploring the model'. (p52)

The Model-based Analysis and Reasoning in Science (MARS) project, reported by Raghavan and Glaser (1995) is considered here since it makes use of interactive computer activities as a central part of the curriculum units that it has developed. However, the major thrust of the project is to develop conceptual understanding and model-based reasoning starting from students' existing ideas and so it could equally be placed in the section on constructivism.

The argument in favour of enabling students to recognise and use theoretical and explanatory models in science is based on the role that these play in the work of scientists and on the advocacy of science educators:

> Scientists and researchers in many disciplines frequently rely on modelling and model-based reasoning to concretise abstract ideas, to simplify and clarify complex phenomena, to predict trends, and to explain mechanisms and processes... Furthermore, national projects working to reform science education recommend that science educators become less

concerned with the presentation of a wide variety of facts and more concerned with overarching themes, and strongly advocate the development of an appreciation for the centrality of models in the teaching and learning of science. (Raghavan and Glaser, 1995, pp37–38)

The use of computer programs means that all students can be provided with similar experiences, which is otherwise less feasible, although theoretically possible. The MARS curriculum material provides a 'script' for students, who work through the activities in pairs. Each topic is introduced through practical activities designed to elicit the students' existing ideas about the concept involved. These are followed by computer-based activities and assignments which introduce the scientific view and give the opportunity for students to grasp and 'play with' the model on the screen. For example, the unit on 'net force' first introduces the idea of using arrows to indicate the direction of a force and a label on the arrow to indicate its strength. Then the computer shows a combination of pushes and / or pulls acting on a ball and the students are challenged to replace the combination by only one force that has the same effect on the ball. They can alter direction and strength of the force and then run their model to see its effect, doing this as often as they wish. After the computer activity they return to practical activity or to a concrete application of the concept. By working through units of this kinds, it is claimed that:

> …students not only learn to deploy models to analyse, predict, and explain phenomena but also recognise the need to modify or extend a model or a system of models and the inherent rules to account for new and increasingly complex situations. (p58)

The teacher's role in these activities is described as being to move around the classroom answering questions, providing help where needed, providing 'appropriate scaffolding', monitoring students' progress, and getting insights into particular difficulties.

The curriculum units were trialled and implemented in five grade 6 (aged 11 / 12) classes and data about the conceptual learning, model-based reasoning and transferability were collected. There was no control group in the study. Preliminary findings indicated that there was an improvement in the students' levels of model understanding, using the levels identified by Grosslight *et al* (1991). However many of the students only used models after being prompted, while some did this spontaneously. Not surprisingly, this was taken as an indication that in order to promote more spontaneous use of models as reasoning tools, appropriate activities should be embedded in science activities more widely. It was also found that more class time was required for the computer-based units than for the same material taught in the regular way. However teachers had more time to circulate and observe students at work, point out inconsistencies, challenge false assumptions and encourage student reflection.

No doubt the computer had an important role in the MARS project because of the facility it provided for making abstract models available for students to manipulate. However this study also pointed to important aspects of any learning experiences which aim at the development of understanding in pupils – the opportunity for students to work out and test out their own ideas and compare them with the scientific view and the role of the teacher in promoting their engagement with ideas and phenomena and reflective thinking.

A project with a similar aim, the Conceptual Change in Science Project, took place in the UK from 1988 to 1991 (O'Shea *et al*, 1993). A combination of computer-based activities and actual practical work was created and implemented in this collaborative project, involving researchers from the University of Glasgow, The Open University and the University of Leeds. The set of activities, designed to teach mechanics to 12 and 13-year-olds, included both a simulation package and computer modelling software. The curriculum materials comprised worksheets for both the computer activities and the conventional laboratory experiments. The simulation program content was determined after extensive study of pupils' prior conceptions of forces and motion. Four 'scenarios' were then designed to address particular preconceptions. For example, the 'cardboard box scenario' was described as follows:

> This illustrates horizontal motion with friction and consists of an object moving horizontally. The object can be accelerated by

a force applied by a human figure and decelerated by sliding friction. Two values of frictional constants, related to the floor of the supermarket and to the rougher surface of the car park, respectively, were available. (O'Shea *et al*, 1993, p181)

Laboratory experiments were designed based on the scenarios, requiring pupils to make predictions, give reasons for their predictions and then check the outcome. After development trials, the materials were implemented for seven weeks with a class of twenty-nine 12-year-olds, spending five hours of class time per week on the materials and using five computers. The class was organised so that pupils worked in threes, spending half their time on practical work and half on the computer program. For comparison there were three control groups who were also studying mechanics, although there was no attempt to match either the pupils or the type and duration of activities. All pupils were given a pre-test, an immediate post-test and a delayed post-test. They were also interviewed about their ideas.

The findings showed 'a significant amount of conceptual change' in the experimental class in the form of a significant increase in the number of correct responses and explanations based on Newtonian theories in both the post-test and delayed post-test. Also the pupils' confidence in their answers increased (since for each question they were asked how sure they were of the answer they gave). There was a decrease in two prior conceptions – the claim that motion implies force, and the neglect of friction as a force opposing motion. However, some new incorrect conceptions appeared. Of the control classes there was one (older by a year than the experimental class) which showed a significant increase in the number of correct responses in the post-test, but no decline in any of the prior misconceptions.

The researchers noted that their results, 'came mostly from the examination of the test data. The analysis of the transcribed interviews provided clear confirmatory evidence in support of this, suggesting that the written test data provide an accurate picture of the pupils' understanding'. Their conclusions include the positive one that, 'it is possible to use simulated computer experiments to augment usefully conventional classroom experiments'. At the same time, there was the depressing finding that the nature of the pupils' conceptions relating to force and motion were very different from the higher levels of understanding assumed in secondary science curricula. The implication for practice is that far greater study time is needed if there is to be the required conceptual change.

Spreadsheets and databases

Spreadsheets can assist in modelling, enabling pupils to change parts of the model step by step. Goodfellow (1990) has described spreadsheets as occupying the middle-ground between simulations and modelling. They also have other functions similar to databases in the manipulation of data that they facilitate. Carson (1997) discusses such uses suitable for age groups 11 to post-16, while Swain (1997) describes the use of a spreadsheet for the simulation of a complex chemical reaction in an activity suitable for post-16 students. Authors and users of databases and spreadsheet programs claim considerable benefits from their use by pupils, particularly in facilitating independent working and collaborative working in groups. However, although some research has involved the use of spreadsheets and databases in connection with other computer programs, it appears that there is little research specifically on the effect of these particular types of program.

Use of the Internet

The use of the Internet is probably the fastest growing area of IT application in schools, as elsewhere. A useful outline of practices, up to 1997, is provided by Jackson and Bazley (1997). It is perhaps premature to look for research into the impact of these new practices on pupils' learning, but it is difficult to imagine that the increased opportunities provided to both pupils and teachers for access to information, for communication and for collaboration will not have a positive effect on teaching and learning. Some of this is evident in the effort being made by schools to make access easy and 'safe' for pupils, as through the downloading of information selectively from the Internet into a school-wide intranet (Diffey, 1997). *School On-Line* is a source of information for both teachers and pupils, offering a question-and-answer area, on-line projects and a useful library of links to various sites.

In Scotland, the *Science On-Line Support Network* (SOLSN) was developed specifically to help primary teachers. It provides an on-line library of selected materials and links to other websites, an e-mail facility which can be used by teachers to ask questions of 'helpers' who have volunteered to respond, opportunities to read others teachers' questions and the responses to them, a notice-board, and the opportunity to exhibit classroom materials and view materials provided by other schools. Developments of this type are multiplying daily but it is too soon to have research evidence of the detail of their impact on science education. An evaluation of the feasibility trials of SOLSN (Harlen and Schilling, 1998) indicated that, despite technical problems which prevented schools from taking full advantage of the SOLSN, teachers were optimistic about the effects on classroom practice. Teachers needed help not only in using the software, but in framing questions to ask and deciding what was suitable materials for posting on the website. Further, the primary teachers felt the need for continued personal contact by phone or visits and so it was suggested that local school clusters provide natural groups of schools to take advantage of the SOLSN facilities, with secondary schools taking an active role in providing information, loaning equipment and working together with its primary schools to improve the quality of science teaching and particularly primary-secondary continuity.

Interactive multimedia

Hartley (1994), in a review of the use of multimedia in science education, quotes the definition of Latchem *et al* (1993) that interactive multimedia means:

> a range of video-disk, compact-disk and computer based systems that allow the creation, integration and manipulation of text, graphics, still and moving images, sound and feedback clues for many diverse applications in education and training, public information and archiving, and point-of-sale and marketing. (p75)

Such a wide selection of stimuli, with the computer combining them in a way that gives the user some control over them, clearly has enormous potential in science education. Not only can there be simulations, but pictures of real places, events and processes, with authentic sound. The importance of pictures has been demonstrated in research by Standing *et al* (1970) who found that a five-second exposure to each of a series of pictures, followed by a recall test, produced more than 90% correct recall even when the number of pictures exceeded 2,500. This visual assistance to memory is used in techniques for remembering which rely on linking words to a visual image. However Bottrill and Lock (1994) found that pictures without sufficient supporting context did not allow the students to make effective use of the visuals; there needs to be a link to both the visual and meaning in words.

Blisset and Atkins (1993) examined the use of video-disc designed to aid understanding of probability and found that 51% of the time was spent 'reading, watching and listening' to the video-disc. Discussion time was largely devoted to what to do to use the video-disc rather than to discussion of the ideas being presented. Similar findings arose from the Conceptual Change in Science Project (see page 27) which developed software to improve students' understanding of motion. Students' discussions were about, for example, how to change graphical displays, and did not necessarily impinge on the students' conceptions. The researchers concluded that the effective use of multimedia in the classroom requires 'the intellectual academic roles of the teacher to remain as important as ever.' These findings are supported by those from research into interactive multimedia in the very different context of a history lesson on World War 2 (Plowman, 1997).

In order to secure the active participation of the student that is necessary to increase learning, multimedia packages may require students to make notes, search for keywords, answer questions, give explanations or solve problems. These requests can made via off-line worksheets but they can also be made on-line so that the whole package of exercises and teaching material provides what is described as an 'electronic workbook'. Hartley (1994) cites the biodiversity project (Williams, 1993) as an example of good use of interactive multimedia:

The context is the study of lichens on headstones in cemeteries in the Yorkshire Dales. These are limestone and the graves also provide information on the dates when they were set in place. The program uses video clips to pan round the locations and still images to show the chosen headstones. The student user can have the system portion the area of the headstone, choose samples, and collect/analyse data showing the diversity and density of lichens. The results are plotted on graphs and given in data-tables. The student also has access to software 'tools' to undertake the measures themselves. Maps and schematics, and hypertext cross-referencing techniques are used to display biological and geographical information. (p84)

Hartley notes that the quantity of such material is not yet very great and that there is need for more evaluative research on how best to use interactive multimedia in teaching and learning.

Some conclusions about using computers

- Science education can benefit from the use of computers for all kinds of applications and for delivering ICT.
- Data-logging and graphing can save time and increase pupils' focus on the meaning of results from practical work rather than on the process of gathering data and drawing graphs. These benefits are found particularly with first and second year secondary pupils and less able pupils.
- Simulations, in combination with practical work, can be effective in helping pupils to change non-scientific conceptions, when they are designed to address these preconceptions, although not all are eliminated.
- Simulations have potential disadvantages in projecting a misleading notion of reality.
- Modelling by students can be helped by computer programs but the teacher's role remains a central one for promoting recognition of false assumptions and encouraging reflection.
- The Internet offers many opportunities, yet to be fully exploited and researched, for both pupils and teachers.
- Interactive multimedia has considerable potential to link different representations and ways of learning to develop understanding in science. However the effective use of this technology makes no less demand on teachers' understanding than conventional classroom activities.

4

Approaches to Constructivism

This section is about cognitive development, that is, bringing about learning with understanding. However, constructivist ideas about learning have such a hold on current views that cognitive development is commonly equated with constructivism in action. Constructivism embraces a very wide range of aspects of teaching, some of which are discussed more fully in later sections on assessment, the use of language and questioning.

Constructivism and learning

More than two decades of research into children's understanding in science have had a considerable impact on views of learning. The first substantial wave of work in this area since Piaget has been well reviewed by Driver and Easley (1978), Driver and Erikson (1983) and Gilbert and Watts (1983). The outcome of this work which is most relevant in the current context is not the details of children's ideas about particular topics, but the consistency in findings of studies from across the world. This has led to universal recognition that pupils are not without ideas about the events and phenomena in the world around them. They do not arrive in the classroom or laboratory with vacant slots in their minds into which new ideas can be poured by teachers, or created by 'discovery' from personal observations. Rather they have their own ideas, but often these are what may be called 'everyday' ideas (Harlen, 1986; Leach and Scott, 1995). Children have formed these ideas in making sense of their everyday experiences because these ideas generally 'work' and are adequate in the context of everyday life.

These everyday ideas are often different from scientific theories and there is much evidence (Tasker, 1981; Champagne et al, 1982; Osborne and Freyberg, 1985; White, 1991) that they interfere in learning science. In Piagetian terms, what often happens is that pupils assimilate new experiences into their present ways of thinking rather than accommodating to new experience by a modification of ideas. Consequently the attention of science educators has turned to how to bring about change or development in ideas, that is, to ensure that children modify their view to accommodate new experience. Piaget suggested that it was necessary to create *disequilibrium* in order to bring about development of ideas. Those who prefer not to use Piagetian terms, on account of disagreement with other aspects of Piaget's theories, speak of the need to create 'dissonance'.

Much research has focused on the various ways of bringing about dissonance in just the right amount, so as to avoid too great a conflict with pupils' ideas or too little challenge, both of which lead to no learning taking place. However, at the same time, research into the nature of pupils' own ideas and reasoning has continued and it is relevant to summarise what is now known about them before proceeding to approaches to change.

Everyday ideas and reasoning

There is some consensus from research studies that the characteristics of children's everyday ideas and ways of thinking which have implications for learning science are as follows:

- Several research studies (eg Claxton, 1993; Millar and Kragh, 1994) have established that these ideas are 'domain-specific'. Children use different ways of explaining events in different situations although these events are scientifically explained by the same idea. For example, young children use different ways of explaining the 'disappearance' of water from clothes on a clothes line, from a puddle on a path or from an uncovered fish tank.

- Children's ideas are influenced by direct everyday experience. As an example, 'we find the bizarre ideas that rust is inside metals waiting to be revealed, based on observation of rust being found under flaking paint or chrome plate' (Harlen, 1997, p104).

- Children are not aware of their ideas as ideas: 'they do not appear to know that their explanations of physical phenomena are hypotheses that can be subjected to experimentation and falsification. Their explanations remain implicit and tacit' (Vosniadou, 1997, p53). This leads to the argument that development of awareness by pupils of their own thinking is important in cognitive development.

- Initial and 'everyday' ideas are not always replaced when conflicting evidence is available; new ideas may be added while children hold on to earlier ideas (Driver, 1983).

- Reasoning is linear, with explanations being given in terms of a cause bringing about an effect in a sequence of time. 'Students explain, for example, that when the plunger of a syringe is pulled out this creates a vacuum. The vacuum then draws liquid into the syringe' (Driver *et al*, 1994, p91). This type of sequential cause-effect reasoning is quite different from that assumed in scientific explanations which are based on relationships often expressed as a model or theory.

Significant work by Driver *et al* (1994) in the project, 'Progression in Children's Ideas about the Nature of Science from age 9 to age 16' has revealed that there is a change with age in these characteristics:

> While we would not postulate a 'natural' development in children's conceptions of physical phenomena, (environmental and cultural influences may clearly vary), evidence does suggests that there are strong commonalties in the trajectories of the reasoning of young people. Results from survey can thus enable the likelihood of particular ideas being used within a group of students of different ages to be anticipated. (p93)

The work of this project will be revisited later in the chapter on curriculum content.

Approaches to changing ideas

Turning to the approaches to creating 'dissonance', Strike and Posner (1985) list four major conditions for bringing about change in ideas:

- there must be dissatisfaction with existing conceptions
- a new conception must be minimally understood, a person must be able to see how experience can be restructured by a new conception
- a new conception must appear initially plausible, to have the capacity to solve problems that provoked dissatisfaction in the old one
- a new conception should suggest the possibility of being fruitful, of opening up new areas of thinking and explanation.

In order for the teacher to know what is likely to meet these conditions it is necessary to find out what the pupils' existing ideas and experiences are. Various teaching sequences have been proposed (Osborne and Freyberg, 1985) all of which begin with some 'scene setting' and proceed to encouraging pupils to describe and explain what they know and think about the subject in hand. The sequence produced by the Children's Learning in Science Project (Driver and Oldham, 1985) is reproduced in Figure 2.

Figure 2: The Children's Learning in Science Project constructivist teaching sequence

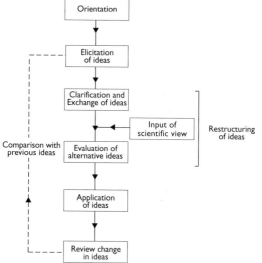

Those parts of this sequence which are concerned with inputting a different view and persuading pupils to accept it remain open to different interpretations. Previously various strategies have been proposed by other researchers for changing pupils' ideas once they have been revealed. An early strategy was to introduce an event or phenomenon which conflicts with the pupils' view in the expectation that the discrepancy would be enough to cause a modification in thinking. It is probably the case that few would regard this as sufficient even if there is only a small gap between the pupils' ideas and those required for scientific understanding. Other ways of using the discrepant event more actively have been suggested, such as following it by group discussions (Erikson, 1970), brainstorming and then debating ideas (Nussbaum and Novick, 1981), charting ideas coming from the class (Shapiro, 1988) and 'interpretative discussion' (Baird and Mitchell, 1986).

Hodson (1993) provides a summary of a sequence of teaching moves (in Figure 3) designed to bring about conceptual development and modification in students' through exploring the extent to which their existing ideas are a basis for explanation and prediction.

Figure 3: Teaching/learning strategies for conceptual development in science (quoted from Hodson, 1993, p108)

i   Making children's own ideas explicit through writing and through discussion with other children and with the teachers.

ii   Exploring the implications of those ideas.

iii   Matching and testing ideas against experience and the experience of others.

iv   Criticising the ideas of others. Subjecting one's own ideas to criticism.

• At this point the teacher should challenge children to find evidence and support for their ideas. Critical interpretation of evidence is the basis for holding to a particular theoretical view in science.

v   Using theoretical ideas to explain observations, phenomena and events.

vi   Applying theoretical ideas to new situations.

vii   Modifying and refining ideas to ensure a better match with 'reality'.

viii   Making predictions. Subjecting theories and predictions to test in the search for support, refutation and refinement.

• At this point the teacher should begin activities designed to effect a shift in understanding.

ix   Introduction of experiences to challenge and contradict children's existing views.

x   Encouraging the generation of alternative conceptual frameworks and explanations by means of 'brainstorming' activities.

xi   Introduction of the 'official' explanatory framework as one of the alternatives – if necessary.

xii   Exploration and testing of all alternatives (repeating steps i–viii).

xiii   Comparison, judgement and selection of the alternative that proves most acceptable to the learning group (including the teacher) ie, reaching consensus – a key step in the practice of science.

• At this point the teacher would embark on a further cycle of conceptual change (ie, proceed to step ix), or would switch to a new topic (ie, proceed to step i).

Throughout these activities the children would be engaged in recording and reporting tasks, using both the 'private' languages of personal exploration and reflection and the 'public' language of scientific communication.

Three cautionary notes about discrepant events are worth adding. Fensham and Kass (1988) point out that what may seem discrepant to the teacher may not be so to the pupil. Moreover, pupils are more tolerant of exceptions to their views than are scientists and so may not see a need to change their ideas simply because an exception has been demonstrated. Solomon and Simpson (1989) raise an objection on more ideological grounds, that the notion of conflict between ideas and the subsequent decision as to which one 'wins' is unsound as a basis for learning. Certainly it would not seem to aid pupils' ownership of ideas.

Watts and Bentley (1987) caution against too direct an assault on pupils' ideas. They emphasise that a non-threatening learning environment is important for learning and that dissatisfaction with existing conceptions is not sufficient motivation for change in ideas. Quoting Strike and Posner (1985) they point out that alternative ideas must not only be seen as 'plausible, intelligible and fruitful', but the process of adopting them involves 'temporary advances, frequent retreats and periods of indecision'. Thus pupils need a good deal of reassurance and a supportive atmosphere if they are to expose their own ideas and publicly change them.

These cautions have particular force at the primary level where much of what pupils encounter is new to them and it is important to build their confidence in being able to make sense of their experiences. Finding out what children's ideas are in order to 'confront' them is not the same as requiring children to use and test their ideas, as a result of which the ideas may be modified or perhaps abandoned in favour of ones which they decide better fit the evidence available. The Science Processes and Concepts Exploration (SPACE) project researched primary pupils' ideas and, working with teachers, developed techniques for helping children to modify their ideas. These:

> ...do not include presenting conflicting or discrepant events and are intended for use in all cases, whether the idea of a child is 'right' or 'wrong'. They include: enabling children to test their own ideas (essentially through using and developing process skills); encouraging generalisation from one context to another; discussing the words children use to describe their ideas;

extending the range of evidence available, requiring children to communicate their ideas. (Harlen, 1992, p499)

One of the areas of uncertainty in constructivism has been the role of the teacher. The ideas of Vygotsky have been embraced in this context since they identify a positive role for the teacher, the learner's peers and others in bringing about development of ideas. Bliss (1995) points out the change that this has brought about:

> Until now the focus in education has always been on children's individual performance. For Vygotsky a true advance in the child's reasoning would be defined as the difference between the child's independent performance and his or her performance in co-operation with a adult. This difference between unassisted and assisted performance generates what Vygotsky calls the zone of proximal development, the movement from the former to the latter showing the child's development potential. (p155)

To date, however, there is no research to show that one approach to changing pupils' ideas is more effective than another nor that any has long-term effects on the development of concepts. According to Adey (1997):

> Even under what might be considered as optimal conditions, in the Children's Learning in Science Project classrooms where an enormous effort is made to engage students in discussions about their own conceptualisations, then to devise critical tests, and to confront preconceptions with evidence, there seems to be no more evidence that higher level concepts are permanently developed than in conventional classrooms. (pp59–60)

This should not, however, be taken as placing a question mark against constructivism. There is convincing evidence from studies of learning in many different areas to support the constructivist view of learning. This is affirmed, for example, at the highest level in the US, in the President's Committee of Advisors on Science and Technology (PCAST) report of 1997. This concluded that:

> Research in the interdisciplinary field of cognitive science, for example, has in recent years provided convincing evidence that the human processing of visual, linguistic and other data entails the active fitting of such input into a rich internal framework of 'real world' knowledge and expectations, and not simply passive

assembly of a mass of external data into an emergent whole. Our understanding of human learning has similarly evolved (based on a wealth of evidence collected over a wide range of different domains and media) from a process based on the passive assimilation of isolated facts to one in which the learner actively formulates and tests hypotheses about the world, adapting, elaborating and refining internal models that are often highly procedural in nature. (PCAST, 1997, section 8.2)

The report further points out that knowledge of the nature of learning is not the same as knowledge of the best way to bring about this learning. How to do this is identified as an important area for future research.

This an appropriate point to turn, in the next chapter, to considering the work of Adey and Shayer who have proposed a different route to concept development.

Some conclusions about constructivism

• There is a sound base of evidence for the existence in pupils of their own constructions about scientific phenomena in the world around, even before they have been exposed to relevant teaching.

• These ideas make sense to the pupils because they are based on everyday experience; but they are also formed through 'everyday' thinking and they often conflict with the scientific view.

• Learning is seen as changing pupils' own ideas into ones consistent with the scientific view.

• Approaches to changing pupils' ideas all begin with some activities which are designed so that pupils express their ideas and make them available to the teacher.

• There is less consensus about how to introduce the scientific view. Approaches vary from facing pupils with a discrepant event, conflicting with their view, to using the pupils' view as a basis for a prediction and testing its validity.

• The arguments of Vygotsky suggest that the teacher has an important role in assisting development and taking the learner further than he or she might be able to go unassisted.

• There is no firm evidence as to the effectiveness of different approaches to developing pupils' ideas within a constructivist framework.

5

Cognitive Acceleration

This approach to improving achievement in science is associated in the UK with the work of Philip Adey and Michael Shayer. Their work in the Cognitive Acceleration through Science Education (CASE) Project is of a quite different order from previous attempts to accelerate cognitive development in that it involved intervention over an extended period of two years and explored short- medium- and longer-term effects and transfer of effects to other subjects across the curriculum. Adey and Shayer's work has been reported in a number of papers and publications (Adey, 1988; Adey and Shayer, 1990; Adey and Shayer, 1993; Adey, Shayer and Yates, 1989; Shayer and Adey, 1992a, 1992b, 1993). The later ones report findings from students followed up three years after the end of the intervention.

The work on cognitive acceleration developed out of their work on Piagetian levels of cognitive development (Shayer and Adey, 1981). They considered that, from the growing knowledge of the course of cognitive development and what affects it, there should be the possibility of finding ways of training which accelerate it. Shayer was particularly influenced by Feuerstein's Instrumental Enrichment Programme (Feuerstein, Rand, Hoffman and Miller, 1980). Large differences between experimental and control groups on a test of Piagetian tasks had been obtained using this programme, although no effects on school achievement had been found. However there was enough evidence to suggest that 'the possibility of teaching general thinking skills was worth pursuing, and that what have recently come to be referred to as Higher Order Thinking Skills (Resnick, 1987) are well characterised by Inhelder and Piaget's descriptions of formal operations' (Adey and Shayer, 1993 p191).

In order to give their idea a practical test they designed a set of intervention activities intended to develop higher levels of thinking. For various reasons, including their own background subject expertise, Adey and Shayer set these activities in a scientific context

41

although they were of the view that the skills were general ones which would help thinking across the curriculum. The 'thinking science' activities focused on the identification and relationship of variables, the use of relationships between variables to make predictions, the presentation of problems designed to induce cognitive conflict, the encouragement of meta-cognition and the explicit linking of thinking strategies to a variety of contexts outside those in which they were being developed:

> Each intervention lesson focuses on one of the schemata (of formal operations, ie control and exclusion of variables, ratio and proportionality, equilibrium, compensation, combinatorial thinking, correlation, probability, compound variables, and conservation involving formal modelling). The terminology required is initially introduced in contexts which require concrete modelling only. Once familiar with terms such as variables, values of variables, and relationships between variables, students are given practical problems which require the use of the formal schema for their solution. There is no attempt to teach, for instance, rules for controlling variables. Rather, the student is put in a position where she has to construct the schema for herself in order to solve a practical problem.
> (Adey and Shayer, 1990, p270)

After piloting in two schools, the activities were given a full two-year trial in seven schools, involving ten experimental classes of 11 and 12-year-olds. Matched control classes were also identified and tested at the same times and using the same tests as the experimental classes. The 'thinking science' lessons were given to the experimental classes by their teachers, replacing a regular science lesson every two weeks for two years. The teachers had been prepared in special training sessions and were visited to check on the way in which the intervention was being operated. Experimental and control classes were tested before intervention (pre-test), immediately after the two-year intervention (immediate post-test), again one year later (delayed post-test) and then their GCSE results were collected. Piagetian Reasoning Tests, developed by Shayer and Adey, were given as pre-test and as part of the post-tests. The post-tests also included science achievement tests developed in collaboration with the teachers to serve as the end of school year tests.

Main findings

Having established no significant difference between control and experimental classes, the results were analysed using regression of the achievement test scores on the pre-test for the control group to predict test scores for the experimental group. This was done separately for the two age groups involved, 11+ and 12+ year-olds at the start, and for boys and girls within these age groups. The differences between the predicted and obtained scores for the experimental groups were then used as the indications of the effect of the intervention.

The results for the immediate post-test on the Piagetian Reasoning Tests showed that significant gains had been made by the 12+ boys and smaller, non-significant, gains by the 12+ girls and the 11+ girls. The results for the 11+ boys showed that only some had gained, whilst overall there had been a decrease compared with the control group. On the science immediate post-tests, there were no significant differences between any experimental and control groups. The authors argued that it would not be expected that transfer would show immediately since pupils would need time and opportunity to apply new skills to further learning.

The results for the delayed post-test, one year after the end of the intervention, showed that the earlier difference between experimental and control groups on the Piagetian Reasoning Tests had disappeared. On the science post-tests there was an increase for all experimental groups which was significant for the 12+ boys and the 11+ girls. Thus the effect on achievement in science appeared to be strengthening and maintaining the same pattern. This result was even more striking in relation to the GCSE results.

In the GSCE science results the 12+ experimental boys were further ahead of the control boys and the difference was also significant for the 11+ girls. Moreover the pupils' GCSE results in mathematics showed a similar pattern of gains as for science. The authors claim that 'this could be taken as evidence for the effect of the intervention on general underlying cognition' (Adey and Shayer, 1993 p208). This claim is further strengthened by the pupils' results on the GCSE English examination. There was a positive gain for the control groups which was significant in all cases except for the 11+

boys. An effect on performance in English was considered reasonable given that the tasks in the examination required analysis of characters and comprehension of texts which could well have been influenced by the intervention activities.

Wider issues

There are important points which follow from this which are of general relevance as well as being specific to science education. The main one concerns the conflicting claims made about the influence of context on learning, focusing on the notion of 'situated cognition'. Those who embrace this notion take the view that the context of a learning activity (not only its subject matter but the situation in which it is encountered) is so important that 'it completely overrides any effect of either the logical structure of the task or the particular general ability of individuals' (Adey, 1997, p51). Evidence to support this often cites examples such as the ability of unschooled young street vendors to calculate accurately while the same young people fail the arithmetic tasks if they are presented in the form of a 'sums' at school. Similar findings have been reported for older people (Nunes *et al*, 1993). Certainly the effect of context on performance has been demonstrated in many studies, notably by Wason and Johnson-Laird (1972). However Adey and Shayer (1994) and Adey (1997) have given spirited responses to these studies, including the well known one of Donaldson (1978) who challenged Piaget's finding by showing that a change in context affected the difficulty of a Piagetian spatial ability task. Adey (1997) argues:

> Clearly motivation and interest play a significant role, and indeed if one wants to get a true picture of the maximum cognitive capability of a child it is essential that the task be made as relevant as possible, and that all of the essential pieces of concrete information are meaningful. But the determined efforts of the situated cognition adherents have failed so far to show that all conceptual difficulties can be accounted for simply by changing the context…. It seems difficult to deny that a significant amount of the variance in children's (and adults') academic performances can be accounted for by some general factors which very different constructs such as 'intelligence', 'schema' and 'style', are trying to capture. (pp59–60)

Adey regards meta-cognition as central to effective learning and suggests that in practice this means teachers talking to pupils about the kinds of difficulties that they have with particular problems and how they think they might overcome these difficulties. Science has a particular role here because of the wide range of problems encountered within it. It therefore provides the opportunity for students to become aware of the general features of problems and thus able to tackle new ones in science and in other subjects. Teachers should encourage pupils to 'reflect on the sort of thinking they have been engaged in, to bring it to the front of their consciousness' (Adey 1997). The importance of making the process a conscious one is so that the pupils become aware of the general aspects of their thinking; they can then lift these out of the particular contexts of learning so that they become useable in other contexts. This is summed up by Perkins and Saloman (1989) as follows:

> The approach that now seems warranted calls for the intimate intermingling of generality and context-specificity in instruction... We forecast that wider-scale efforts to join subject-matter instruction and the teaching of thinking will be one of the exciting stories of the next decade of research and educational innovation. (see Adey, 1997, p85)

Some conclusions about cognitive acceleration

- The Cognitive Acceleration in Science Education (CASE) is a programme of interventions designed to develop formal operational thinking.
- The effect of CASE activities on performance has been thoroughly investigated, more so than for many other types of intervention.
- Long-term effects have been shown in terms of raised achievement in mathematics and English as well as in science.
- There is no suggestion that CASE-type work should replace teaching of content in science but as a supplement there is evidence that it can have beneficial effects.
- Its success depends on the teachers undergoing special training.
- Certain aspects of the CASE approach, particularly meta-cognition and linking thinking strategies to problems in different contexts, find support from other studies of effective teaching where they appear to be among the key factors.

6

Assessment

Assessment of students has a number of different purposes which can be spread along a dimension from directly helping teaching and learning to summarising and certificating achievement at a particular time. Some summative assessment is used for evaluative or accountability purposes. The concern in the present context is with assessment which affects teaching and learning and, while it can be argued that certification and accountability have an influence on these, the main direct influence is from formative assessment and so the discussion here will be restricted to this.

The definition used by Black and Wiliam (1998a) identifies the key components of formative assessment:

> ...the term 'assessment' refers to all those activities undertaken by teachers, *and by their students in assessing themselves*, which provide information to be used as feedback to modify the teaching and learning activities in which they are engaged. *Such assessment becomes 'formative assessment' when the evidence is actually used to adapt the teaching work to meet the needs.* (p2) (Emphases in original).

Formative assessment in this sense is clearly central to constructivist teaching since this involves finding out pupils' initial ideas and skills. Similarly it is implied in all child-centred work following the Plowden principle to 'begin where the child is'.

However Paul Black (1993) questioned Harry Black's (1986) claim that formative assessment has always been part of the practice of teachers. Indeed Harry Black himself reported a survey of assessment policies in Scotland which showed that only 29% of schools had a policy on non-reported assessment whilst 87% had one for reported assessment. An even smaller percentage (about 8%) included non-reported assessment in a written policy.

The practice of formative assessment is very varied. It often takes the form of short teacher-made tests and although there is evidence that feedback from such tests can improve learning (Scheerens, 1991) the validity of such tests is often suspect. They frequently do not reflect the complexity of ideas or skills that the teaching is intended to develop (Resnick and Resnick, 1992). However Black (1993) cites various studies which show that written questions do improve students' learning in a variety of contexts:

> ... in traditional lessons (Ehindero, 1985), with computer-animated lessons (Holliday and McGuire, 1992), with self-study of texts (Sugerman and Mayer, 1988) and in learning from chart representations (Holliday and Benson, 1991). Questions seem to help by promoting selective attention, by cueing retrieval and by guiding mental editing of new knowledge. (pp72–73)

A meta-analysis of 40 studies by Bangert-Drowns *et al* (1991) showed performance on external tests does improve with enhanced use of classroom testing. The findings of these studies have to be treated with caution as long as the details are unknown and the possibility remains that the classroom testing was in effect drilling for the external tests.

While traditional written questions may continue to have a role, it has been recognised in the US particularly (Raizen *et al*, 1989, 1990) that new methods of teaching in science require a change in methods of assessment. In the UK, a programme which combined assessment and the development of process skills at the primary school level was given extensive trials and led to the publication of books for teachers on written (Schilling *et al*, 1990) and practical tasks (Russell and Harlen, 1990). Other materials have been produced to help teachers with new methods of assessment, matching new approaches to teaching (eg in the UK, SCRE, 1995; Harlen and Jelly, 1997; and in the US, Hein, 1991). However, as Black points out, such materials are in need of rigorous evaluation. He suggests it is necessary to determine whether they can satisfy important conditions: of classroom feasibility, reliability, validity, absence of bias, attention to motivational and affective as well as cognitive development and ways to develop pupil self-assessment (Black, 1993, p76).

Deficiencies of current practice

Black and Wiliam (1998a, 1998b) reviewed evidence relating to current practice, drawing on the reviews by Black (1993) and Crooks (1988). They listed the following shortcomings of existing approaches, which are quoted (from Black and Wiliam, 1998a, pp4–5) in full since not only do they resonate with experience but they suggest ways in which practice can be improved:

- Teachers' tests encourage rote and superficial learning: this is seen even where teachers say they want to develop understanding – and many seem unaware of the inconsistency.
- The questions and other methods used are not discussed with or shared between teachers in the same school and are not critically reviewed in relation to what they actually test.
- For primary teachers particularly, there is a tendency to emphasise quantity and presentation of work and to neglect its quality in relation to learning.
- The giving of marks and the grading functions are over-emphasised, while the giving of useful advice and the learning function are under-emphasised.
- Approaches are commonly used in which pupils are compared with one another, the prime purpose of which appears to them to be competition rather than personal improvement.
- Teachers' feedback to pupils often seems to serve social and managerial functions, at the expense of the learning functions.
- Teachers are often able to predict pupils' results on external tests – because their own tests imitate them – but at the same time they know too little about their pupils' learning needs.
- The collection of marks to fill up records is given greater priority than the analysis of pupils' work to discern learning needs; furthermore, some teachers pay no attention to the assessment records of previous teachers of their pupils.

Gains from improved assessment practice

However, despite the shortcomings of existing practice, Black and Wiliam did find strong evidence that '…formative assessment is an essential feature of classroom work and the development of it can raise standards' (p19). In their review, Black and Wiliam helpfully reported evidence for this claim and also identified significant features of the operation of formative assessment that appear to make it effective in improving learning.

The evidence from at least 20 studies is remarkably consistent in pointing to substantial and significant gains from innovations which include strengthening the practice of formative assessment. Black and Wiliam (1998a) calculate that the size of the effect on performance is larger than for most other educational interventions – for example, it would raise the position of a pupil from among the average to being in the top 35%. Some studies involved children with mild learning difficulties and these children benefited particularly from the improved formative assessment. The possibility of reducing the spread of attainment is a feature which deserves serious attention, given the greater spread of achievement in Scotland compared with other countries (as noted in this review, p3). Black and Wiliam concluded from the evidence they reviewed that:

> it seems clear that very significant gains could lie within our grasp. The fact that such gains have been achieved by a variety of methods which have, as a common feature, enhanced formative assessment, indicates that it is this feature which accounts, at least in part, for the successes. (Black and Wiliam, 1998a, p4)

At the same time these researchers pointed out the considerable difficulties of widespread adoption and take-up of formative assessment since several features of effective formative assessment require quite fundamental shifts in teachers' views of how children learn and, particularly, the benefits of giving the pupils a role in their own assessment. On this point Black (1993) makes the cogent comment that:

> Teachers need the confidence that they can make anyone learn as long as they go about it the right way, confidence that is needed because devotion to formative assessment is risky, taking a great deal of time and energy. In particular, since many pupils may have acquired the habit of doing just enough to get by, or have ceased to believe that they can be competent at the subject, the contract between teacher and pupil has to be reformulated. (p79)

Towards better assessment

On the basis of their review Black and Wiliam make suggestions as to how formative assessment can be improved. These are discussed under three headings: the self-esteem of pupils; self-assessment by pupils; and the evolution of effective teaching.

In relation to self-esteem, the main point arises from the form in which assessment is reported to the pupils. Where this is in terms of grades or ranking within the class then 'pupils look for the ways to obtain the best marks rather than at the needs of their learning which these marks ought to reflect'. Research has given many examples of how pupils spend time looking for clues to the 'right' answer and for the easiest ways to obtain credit. Moreover those who get poor results feel that this is a judgement of their ability and they can do nothing about it. These negative effects can be avoided by giving feedback only about the particular aspects of the work, with discussion on how it can be improved and making no judgemental comment on the child as a person or in comparison with others.

Self-assessment is still at an early stage of development but Black and Wiliam regard it as an essential part of formative assessment. Sadler (1989) is quoted by Black and Wiliam as helping understanding of the role of self-assessment in learning by identifying three necessary elements of feedback on learning: knowing what the desired goal is, knowing where one is in relation to this goal and knowing how to close the gap. The extent of good practice in implementing these forms of feedback is limited, but Black and Wiliam (1998a) claim that:

> When pupils do acquire such overview, they then become more committed and more effective as learners: their own assessments become an object of discussion with their teachers and with one another, and this promotes even further that reflection on one's own ideas that is essential to good learning. (p10)

In relation to improving practice, the outcomes of their review lead Black and Wiliam to emphasise planning which includes formative assessment. 'Tasks have to be justified in terms of the learning aims that they serve, and they can only work well if opportunities for pupils to communicate their evolving understanding are built into the planning' (p10). There are also implications for teachers' questioning and the kind of dialogue between teacher and pupils, which 'should be thoughtful, reflective, focused to evoke and explore understanding, and conducted so that all pupils have an opportunity to think and to express their ideas' (p12). In addition, classroom tests and homework exercises should reflect the learning aims and feedback on them should be given to pupils following the principles already mentioned. Research has clearly shown that feedback in the form of comments *only* (with no judgemental grade or symbol), leads to higher achievement as compared with feedback in terms of grades or praise or no feedback at all (Butler, 1987).

Some conclusions about assessment

- This part of the review has focused on formative assessment, that is, assessment designed to assist teaching and learning.
- There is evidence that improving formative assessment can raise standards in a wide range of different learning contexts.
- Assessment is only formative when it reflects the aims of learning and is used in making decisions about the next steps in learning.
- Current practice lacks many of the features which research shows are central to a positive impact on achievement.
- Feedback to pupils is important so that they can take part in deciding how to improve their performance and should be of the form which makes this possible.
- Effective feedback focuses on the work and does not make judgements about the ability of the pupil or comparisons with other pupils.
- Planning what is to be assessed and how to do it is an important part of teachers' preparation.
- There is need for further research on the effectiveness of published assessment materials.

7

Planning, Questioning and Using Language

Many of the foregoing sections have touched upon planning, questioning and the use of language as features of effective teaching. They symptomise rather than determine good practice, as illustrated by returning to the study by Garnett and Tobin (1988) of two teachers with different styles but both effective in developing understanding in their pupils. Although they were teaching in the upper secondary school, the characteristics they showed are relevant to all teaching.

Garnett and Tobin concluded that the following were significant features of teaching although implemented in different ways by the two teachers (see p16 above).

- They both placed emphasis on students' understanding. In different ways the teachers ensured that new material was linked to students' existing ideas and was understood.
- They both used three different types of monitoring: they anticipated disruptive behaviours; they checked on student engagement by circulating round the class during small group work; they checked on students' developing understanding by questioning and inviting questions from the students.
- The provision of feedback on learning was constantly provided to the students through formal means (exercises and tests) and informal means (teacher questioning in both whole class and individual student-teacher interaction).
- The teachers' understanding of their subject-matter was very solid.
- They managed their classes so that there was minimum wastage of class time and high levels of engagement.
- They encouraged students to raise questions and responded to them without making the students feel stupid.

The emphasis on developing students' understanding is a feature of science teaching that several studies have found to be missing in teachers' practice. For example, Mitman *et al* (1984) studied 11 junior high school science classes and found that few of the tasks the students were given demanded high level thinking skills and that the kinds of assessment given most weight were tests of low cognitive demand. The reason for the tendency of teachers to reduce the level of cognitive demand was illuminated by Gallagher and Tobin (1987) who found that when the cognitive demand of the work was high students indulged in off-task behaviour which caused class management problems. Teachers reduced the demand to cope with this. Thus it is important to combine a high level of demand with the monitoring procedures needed for maintaining task engagement and which also ensure that the level of demand is not so high as to endanger understanding.

Planning

Much of the work reported variously by Tobin, Garnett and Gallagher drew on the Exemplary Practice in Science and Mathematics Education project in Western Australia (see p16). It included case-studies of primary teachers as well as those of high school science teachers. The observed teaching of two primary teachers reported by Tobin and Garnett (1988) showed several problems in the context of what would hardly be described as 'exemplary' practice, but which, as the authors point out, is probably better than most:

> Two problems emerged regarding Richard's teaching practices. In small group activities classroom management was problematic, and during whole-class activities, interactions were dominated by a few target students. Improvements in these two areas could result in enhanced learning opportunities for all students.

> Graham had other problems.... Although he monitored student behaviour, he did not monitor student thinking. He moved about the room attending to administrative matters, leaving students to construct their own knowledge without teacher cues or feedback. In some groups certain individuals monopolised the use of materials and prevented others from manipulating the

pins and straws... At the end of the data-collecting activity Graham asked students to pack away the equipment. There was no time allowed for discussion of results. (p102)

These studies show how important it is to have evidence from direct observation in classrooms in order to identify whether learning is being effectively promoted and, if so, how, and if not, why not, in order to be able to use research in improving classroom practice.

It was clear from the examples which the Australian studies provided that the primary teachers had not planned beforehand what the children were to learn from the activities. Thus is was hardly likely that the children would have any idea of the aims of their work and as a consequence they would be in no position to direct their own learning. Tobin and Garnett concluded that the failure of the teachers to focus on development of ideas about the content of the activity may have led to the increased incidence of off-task behaviours as the activity progressed.

In their analysis Tobin and Garnett also emphasised the effect of the primary teachers' low level of understanding in science. Clearly this can be addressed only slowly (eg by raising the level of science required in the background of entrants to primary teaching or providing more science in the training courses). Meanwhile measures have to be taken to alleviate the problem for those currently in the classroom. Planning, and support for planning, emerge as features of primary science practice in need of improvement and where action might well pay dividends. Current planning, as Palmer (1997) has demonstrated, focuses on what children will *do* and not on what they will *learn* nor on how *the teacher* will facilitate children's learning. Better planning would include:

- what ideas the activity would help to develop
- what skills the activity would help to develop
- how the children's initial ideas would be elicited
- what questions the teacher would ask, when and for what purpose (including asking children what they would like to find out)
- what classroom organisations are appropriate at different points of the lesson

- what equipment is needed
- what and how instructions would be given to the children
- how the children will record and report their activities
- how the plenary discussions will be handled
- how any change in children's ideas and skills will be monitored.

While planning this amount of detail may seem a tall order for many teachers it is difficult to see how effective teaching can proceed without at least the factors listed above being thought through beforehand. The initial steps require teachers themselves to understand the concepts involved in the pupils activities. If they don't have this knowledge it is available in books specifically written for primary teachers (eg Nuffield Primary Science, 1997). Using these and other sources (such as the CD produced in Scotland), as the need arises, could gradually improve background understanding without teachers feeling the need to learn about all areas of science before they can begin. (See also Chapter 9)

Teachers' questions

The quality of teacher's questions has been the subject of several studies. For example, Stiggins *et al* (1989) studied the classroom work of 36 teachers by observation, reading documents and by interviews. They found that the questioning of the teachers at all levels was dominated by recall questions. This was the case even for those who had been trained to teach higher level thinking skills, although these teachers did ask more relevant questions. In science lessons, 65% of questions asked for recall and there were only 17% requiring inferential and deductive reasoning. Galton, Simon and Croll's (1980) study of primary classrooms in England found that 5% of teachers' questions could be categorised as 'open' while 22% were closed and 30% required recall of specific facts.

The reasons for deploring this situation have been articulated by Shapiro (1998). Commenting on the patterns of dialogue observed in classrooms, where teachers question in order to 'pull the ideas that she wants from the children', Shapiro points out that this gives no opportunity for the teacher to find out about the pupils' ideas. Moreover the pattern of teachers' question-and-answer 'itself controls student behaviour and enforces rules of interaction that makes science learning into a kind of game in which learners attempt to guess the ideas that she is thinking' (p617).

Thus teaching that is concerned with learners developing their understanding has to avoid closed, low-level questions which take away the learners' control for developing their own ideas. Types of questions which help rather than hinder this development are, in form, open and person-centred (SCRE, 1995) and, in content, require reasoning skills, prediction, interpretation and argument.

The quality of teachers' questions has been related to teachers' knowledge of the subject-matter. Carlsen (1987) showed that teachers with high content knowledge ask fewer questions and encourage more questions. Low levels of teacher understanding of the subject matter were related to asking low-level questions designed to serve the purposes of classroom management. Carlsen also showed that teachers are more likely to use whole class teaching for topics where they have greater knowledge of the subject matter. This would seem to support the findings of Harlen, Holroyd and Byrne (1995) that primary teachers, whose understanding and confidence in teaching science is low, tend to avoid whole class discussions.

Pupils' questions

The importance of encouraging pupils to ask questions has been pointed out by several science educators (eg Jelly, 1985). Watts *et al* (1997) have further emphasised the role of pupils' questions in helping teachers to diagnose understanding:

> Our suggestion is that there are periods in the process of learning – the learning of school science in this case – where learners will form fixed and tight definitions, concepts, frameworks, and so on. There are other periods when pupils' thinking on the issues becomes loose, more flexible and open to change. Both periods are important so it is essential to fix some ideas so that progress can be made on the next. However, the teacher can appreciate 'where the pupil is at' through the quality of the questions the child asks. (p62)

Through the study of pupils' questions Watts *et al* identified three categories which can be used for this diagnosis. These are, first, *consolidation,* where pupils are moving toward consolidation of their ideas on a particular subject. Questions of this kind express what pupils think and ask for confirmation of their explanations. The second type are questions for *exploration* where ideas are quite firmly held and are used to make predictions which the pupils are seeking to test in the questions asked. The third type, *elaboration*, are asked when pupils are making up their minds about certain ideas and are examining pros and cons.

These authors recognised that encouraging pupils to ask questions may be disruptive to lesson plans and so propose strategies for dealing with such interruptions without discouraging questioning. These include a specific time for free questioning within a lesson, a 'question box' in the classroom, pupils asking questions of each other in a turn-taking structure and 'question-making' homework.

Although Watts *et al* did not investigate any effect of question-raising on student achievement, there have been several studies in the US of such effects. Black and Wiliam (1998b) cite a study by King with 5th grade students in the context of problem-solving on computer-administered tasks:

> With a sample of 46 students, one group was given no extra instruction, another was trained to ask and answer questions with student partners, whilst a third group were also trained in questioning one another in pairs but directed to use strategic questions for guidance in cognitive and meta-cognitive activity. The latter training focused on the used of generic questions such as How are X and Y alike? and What would happen if...? The outcome was measured by a post-test of written problems and a novel computer task. The group trained to ask strategic questions of one another out-performed the others. (p33)

However Black and Wiliam also quote a meta-analysis of various studies designed to promote higher-order thinking and self-regulation of their study by students through the generation of questions, some through peer interaction and some through more direct instruction. The conclusion is that there is evidence of strong effects of experience of question generation on pupils' achievement, the size of the effect depending on the outcome measure used. There was no advantage of using peer interaction compared with direct instruction in question generation.

Using language: talking

The work of Barnes (1976) in drawing attention to the importance of talking to develop learning has lost none of its relevance. He was concerned with language in all settings, both in discussion among pupils and between pupils and teacher. By studying children's speech when involved in group tasks, Barnes showed how individuals contribute to the shared understanding of an event or process. One pupil's idea may be taken up by another and elaborated; it may perhaps be challenged by someone else and lead to the group seeking evidence to see which idea stands up to being tested. With several minds at work there is less chance of ideas being tested in a superficial manner than if a pupil is working alone with no-one to challenge how things are done. The challenge can only be made if the thinking is public, that is, through talk which is under the control of the pupils. Encouraging genuine collaborative group activity is important to achieving the kind of interchange which develops ideas. Barnes also pointed out that working in groups, of itself, will not serve this purpose. There has to be a structure which facilitates learners' reflection on what they have done and requires experience of 'representing' it to themselves. He added:

> There seems every reason for group practical work...normally to be followed by discussion of the implications of what has been done and observed, since without this what had been half understood may soon slip away. Talk and writing provide means by which children are able to reflect upon the bases upon which they are interpreting reality, and thereby change them. (p31)

Henderson (1994) has suggested several strategies for promoting group collaboration and class discussion, including:

- groups researching a topic and presenting their findings to the rest of the class
- groups discussing their ideas and presenting a short talk or a poster
- groups planning an investigation and sharing ideas with the rest of the class

• groups interpreting information in the form of graphs or tables and presenting their findings to others.

Using language: writing

Rowell (1997) also touched on the role of spoken language in a review which was mainly concerned with research into writing in science. She noted that the strong influence of Vygotsky's theory that learning is socially mediated, leads to the view that:

> ...beginners move from dialogue with more experienced persons to private speech, and eventually to independent cognitive activity. Cognition is interpersonal before is it intrapersonal; thus the construction of meaning (learning) is influenced to a large extent by the social and interactional experiences in which language is developed. (p23)

Thus, although writing is usually an individual activity, the form and content of writing 'is shaped by the community around us'. Advocates of using writing to help the development of understanding in science emphasise its potential in helping learners to 'make meaning'. Pupils who are asked to write 'in their own words' are expected to use this opportunity to make their own sense of some event or phenomena that they are describing. In practice, however, most experience of this 'expressive' writing is that it often misses the focus of the particular ideas which are to be learned. There are also those who claim that science is a language of its own and 'cannot be understood in your own words' (Martin, 1990, p113). This view is that writing in science is a particular genre and that students have to learn how to do it and how particular forms of writing serve the purposes of science. The notion of 'writing frames' developed by Lewis and Wray (1996, 1998) has been adapted by several schools and local authorities to support writing in science.

Research evidence suggests that few pupils are taught these skills. The APU (Assessment of Performance Unit) surveys (Gorman *et al*, 1988) found that the writing of more than 70% of 11-year-olds was poor when asked to plan a science investigation. In a study carried out in South Australia, Laslett *et al* (1992) found that performance on writing a report of a science activity was the lowest of all the writing tasks. One reason for this, as Rowell found, may well be the prevalence in primary classes of worksheets which provide a structure for reporting and remove the need to think about and practice the form of a report. Evidence from NAEP (National Assessment of Educational Performance) and APU surveys indicates that this may be equally apply at the secondary level.

When writing is incorporated in students' work, does it affect their learning? Rowell quoted a study by Langer and Applebee (1987) who:

> Claimed to have clear evidence that different kinds of writing activities do lead students to focus on different kinds of information and to think about that information in different ways. (p37)

However she cautions against drawing sweeping conclusions from these studies:

> We could conclude that, at present, these is little empirical evidence to support the belief that writing *alone* serves as a mode of learning. Empirical studies which claim that meaning-making and / or knowledge restructuring results from writing activities have not isolated the writing from the other features of the classroom. This would suggest that, without appropriate contextual scaffolding, that is, interactions among students and teachers which are oriented towards development of ideas and processes in science, the promises of writing to learn are unlikely to be fulfilled. (p42)

Henderson and Wellington (1998) support the view that the style of conventional scientific writing may be a barrier for the majority of pupils and advocate and illustrate:

> Exploring different ways of getting pupils to present written records of their investigations and observations and to give them the opportunity of showing that they understand a scientific topic or concept. (p38)

They also make an important point about vocabulary in science, that it is not just technical words that can present a barrier to learning, but also that non-technical words commonly used in science are often misunderstood. They quote a study by Gardner in Australia which explored the understanding of pupils aged 12 to 15 of a long list of such words. Less than half of the 12-year-olds understood 'average', 'composition', 'concept', 'contract', 'illuminate', 'factor', 'partial'; 'rate', 'valid', for example and these words still gave trouble to one third of 14-year-olds (Gardner, 1972).

As for the technical words, Henderson and Wellington suggest the development of a 'word bank' of important and commonly used words in science which could be displayed as a poster in the laboratory and kept as lists in the pupils' books or files. The purposes identified for such a bank were:

- as a guide to pupils and teachers to the key words of the science curriculum for 11 to 16-year-olds
- as a spell checker (and a key word list) for pupils when writing up science work; and also for teachers when writing on the board/OHP or preparing worksheets
- as a revision aid for pupils and teachers..
- as a memory jogger for pupils when writing, and for teachers when teaching and writing materials for pupils
- as a way of highlighting the key words of science
- to help pupils with limited reading skills develop a subject-specific 'sight'. (p41)

Some conclusions about planning, questioning and using language

- Pupils' learning is supported most effectively when teachers have planned lessons carefully towards the development of identified skills and understanding, that is, when they know what they want pupils to learn.
- Teachers may make too few demands on higher-level thinking in lower secondary classes in response to pupils' reactions; it is easier to keep pupils on task when the cognitive demand is lower.
- Greater demands on pupils have to be matched by effective monitoring in classrooms to ensure pupils' engagement with tasks, encourage and answer their questions and support their development of understanding.
- Opportunities for pupils to raise questions provide teachers with access to pupils' ideas; higher achievements are associated with pupils asking strategic questions.

- Teachers' questions which are open and demand higher levels of thinking encourage higher achievement in pupils.
- Teachers' planning should focus on what teachers will do and what pupils are intended to learn as well as on what pupils will do.
- When pupils work in groups the evidence suggests that learning is increased when tasks are structured to promote collaboration and are followed by whole-class discussion.
- Pupils need help as well as the opportunity to write about their findings and ideas in their own words.
- Non-technical words used in the context of science can be as confusing as technical words and teachers need to ensure that pupils share their understanding of the vocabulary used.

8

The Curriculum

It is probably true that all the research studies conducted to reveal pupils' conceptions about the scientific aspects of the world around have potential implications for curriculum planning. These implications may not be brought out explicitly, partly because they sometimes focus on children's ideas when no attempt has been made to influence these ideas through teaching and partly because they pick out certain age groups and have little to say about what comes before or after. The studies selected for review in this section are chosen for specific focus on implications for current curriculum content and for concern across the ages of eight to fourteen years.

Reasoning skills and curriculum planning

Johnstone *et al* (1997) assessed children from P4 to S2 (eight to fourteen years) in Scotland using tasks which involved reasoning chains of varying lengths. The researchers were convinced, 'that the very essence of science is in its cause-and-effect reasoning in response to questions which we pose about the natural world'. They were led to recognising the importance of these reasoning chains from noting that much work on children's reasoning had been in question-and-answer sequences where, 'the pupil is effectively prompted along a reasoning chain one link at a time'. Their work addressed the question of whether children could, unaided, construct extended reasoning chains.

The researchers constructed ten tasks involving reasoning chains of varying lengths which were given to 36 children from six age groups in individual interviews. They accepted as 'correct' any relevant train of reasoning including 'children's science' as well as what was acceptable as formal scientific explanation. Averaging the lengths of reasoning chains over the 10 tasks, they found a steady but slow change of reasoning chain length with age and from lower ability to higher ability pupils within each age group. The conclusions they drew from their study were that some pupils, particularly in upper primary and lower secondary classes, will find difficulty with the parts of the science curriculum which involve multi-step reasoning and that, 'it may be necessary to deal with simple one-step cause-and-effect phenomena or to accept the "beginning and end" interpretations of more complex phenomena'. This latter point refers to a finding from an earlier study by the same researchers who analysed children's explanations of certain phenomena chosen on account of being intriguing and thought-provoking to young children. These children worked in pairs without an adult present and their discussions were recorded. Johnstone *et al* (1997) found that:

> The 'explanations' arising from over 100 children in eight schools over the age range 8–11 had clear characteristics:
>
> • They were often scientifically non-acceptable explanations, but they had a logical consistency of their own.
> • They were often incomplete (even among the oldest pupils concentrating either on the beginning or the end of the cause-and-effect chain).
> • In many cases the beginning and end of a chain were stated with nothing in the middle, for example: 'The steam engine goes because you put the fire under it'. This, of course, has its own logic and in everyday life may be quite sufficient....' (p74)

Importantly, when this study was extended to pupils in the first two years of secondary school, these pupils gave explanations with far more complete reasoning chains, but only for those phenomena which has been the subject of formal teaching. In the cases of the phenomena which were unfamiliar to them, 'they were little better than primary school children at constructing reasoning chains'.

This research points to the importance of considering the reasoning demands of explaining various phenomena. While pupils may be able to follow a chain of reasoning when it has been drawn out for them, this does not mean that their spontaneous reasoning is always so detailed.

Understanding of concepts and curriculum planning

Driver *et al* (1994) provided an important review of cross-age studies of children's conceptual development in science from which they drew implications for curriculum construction. They made two different but equally significant points from this review. The first was that there are differences related to age in the ways children reason, in what they regard as real (their ontologies) and in their understanding of scientific enquiry. The second was that how these change with age influence the development of particular ideas is specific to what they call the 'domains' of science in which ideas have been studied, for example mechanics, light and sound, matter, biological inheritance, plant nutrition and ecology.

In following the line of thinking from this study it is useful to have an example in mind. The study by Leach *et al* (1994) is described by Driver *et al* (1994) as follows:

> This study investigated the ideas of school students aged 5 to 16 years about a number of aspects of the interdependence of living things, including cycling of matter and energy. A range of interview and written tasks was devised to probe these aspects. About 450 students, across the age range 8/9 to 15/16 responded to written tasks and a smaller number were interviewed across that age range....One aspect focused on was the process of decay and the cycling of matter. In one of the tasks, students were presented with a photograph of a rotting apple on the ground below an apple tree and they were asked to say what happens when the apple rots. A number of the youngest children in the study appeared quite unfamiliar with the phenomenon of decay. For the remainder, rotting was seen as 'rotting away' – a dead organism rots and leaves no material products. This lack of conservation of matter was also noted in students' reasoning about other biological processes such as growth. Students in the upper primary and lower secondary years typically talked about rotting things giving 'fertility' to the soil. Air or gases were not generally included in their explanations of chemical processes involving living things. The most sophisticated view, held by a minority of the oldest students, involved an appreciation of conservation of matter in decay and the role of decomposers in returning matter into the environment. In this example, we see that the evolution of more sophisticated concepts of decay required students to consider living material as behaving by the same laws as other material

substances and to make connection with a larger range of other relevant knowledge. (p83)

These researchers were at pains to point out that cross-age studies are not the same as longitudinal studies, but, at the same time, they do 'indicate in broad terms the nature of the changes in reasoning which may be demonstrated by students in particular curricular settings' (p86). They also emphasised that they were not postulating a universal natural sequence of development across the whole of science but that what is found is domain-specific and can be used to inform decisions about curriculum sequencing within specific domains. Thus charting the evolution of students' ideas within particular scientific domains is an important role for research.

The domain relevance is brought out in the example of ideas about decay of living material just quoted. Here the conservation of matter is an important aspect in developing scientific understanding. Conservation of matter is involved in the development of other ideas, such as understanding what happens when things burn or when water evaporates. But in the context of living things the notion of conservation is confused by a common view among children that living material is different in kind from other substances. Thus ability to conserve matter in the context of non-living material would not mean that children would conserve matter in the case of changes in living things (growth and decay).

What has been established, according to Driver *et al*, is that there is now enough evidence of commonality between what they call the 'conceptual trajectories' of different students that it is possible to use research evidence in planning and sequencing the curriculum. They offer the following example of how this can operate in practice in the context of explaining how matter is cycled in ecosystems:

> The structure of the subject matter...suggests that a curricular sequence for teaching about matter cycling will require the cellular processes, decay and the relationships between organisms to be introduced at some level prior to full explanations of matter cycling. However, it is apparent from research that students face challenges in understanding these component processes. In the case of the process of decay, for example, research evidence (see Leach *et al*, 1994) suggests that

many students between the ages of five and seven are unfamiliar with some of the phenomena relating to the decay process. From the age of seven, however, a number do refer to decay as enriching the soil in some way. An appropriate early step in a curriculum aiming for understanding of matter cycling therefore involves ensuring the familiarity of students with appropriate phenomena involving decay. Following this, an appreciation of the conservation of matter is then an essential pre-requisite to understanding matter cycling.

Many students below the age of seven do not appear to conserve matter in their explanations of processes such as decay and growth, assuming that matter can appear and disappear. Studies suggest that students accept matter conservation involving the solid and the liquid state before they develop a stable notion of gas-as-matter....For this reason, it is likely that early teaching about matter cycling will be better understood initially in contexts which do not involve gases. For example, in the decay process, the cycling of matter via the soil is likely to be grasped more readily than the cycling of matter via the atmosphere. (pp94–95)

Subject status and curriculum planning

A study by Littledyke (1997) has some relevance in the Scottish curriculum context insofar as a goal of Environmental Studies is environmental education. He investigated the priorities, practices and concerns in science and environmental education of primary school staff in England, where science has the high status of a compulsory core subject and environmental education, as a cross-curricular theme, has a lower status and the chance of being squeezed out. The findings of a survey of primary schools showed that 100% of schools had policy statements in science whilst environmental education policy statements existed in only 27% of schools and most of these were included in the statements of other subjects. In terms of resources, there had been significant increases in science resources since the inception of the National Curriculum, but few schools provided budgetary support for environmental education despite giving it a high rating for importance.

Littledyke also investigated attitudes and confidence in relation to teaching science and interest in environmental education. Confidence and positive attitudes towards science were associated with positive attitudes to environmental education and a good understanding of the issues. Positive attitudes to environmental education were also found in teachers who emphasised processes in science. Teachers whose preferred teaching style was less child-centred and had less emphasis on process and values, showed low interest in and negative attitudes towards science and low interest in environmental issues. The author identified (p655) both those factors which promoted and those which inhibited environmental education, the latter including:

- lack of scientific understanding of environmental issues in many teachers

- limited concern for or interest in environmental education in some teachers

- inappropriate or limited understanding of the nature of science and its role in environmental problems

- approaches to teaching which can perpetuate inappropriate understanding of science in children.

The implications drawn from this research in the English context were that, 'confidence in science can enhance understanding of environmental issues and provide an important platform for environmental education'. Thus, development of environmental education should be seen as being supported by corresponding development of teachers' understanding of science and confidence in science teaching.

Some conclusions about the curriculum

- Attention should be given to the complexity of the reasoning which is demanded for understanding particular phenomena when deciding where these should be placed within the curriculum framework.

- There is evidence that some ideas common across science are more easily developed in some content areas than others and their generalisation should not be assumed.

- Research evidence about the conceptual development of pupils should be used in planning and sequencing curriculum guidelines.

- Understanding and confidence in teaching science appears to be an important factor in effective teaching of environmental education.

9

Teachers' Understanding of Science

Research into teachers' understanding of science and its effect on classroom activities has focused on primary teachers, although there is informal agreement that similar problems exist in secondary science where an area of science is taught by someone specialising in a different area of science (Ratcliffe, 1998). Bishop and Denley (1997) have voiced concerns about what they see as subject-matter being squeezed out of PGCE courses for secondary teachers. However the main concern is for primary science teaching and the research has concerned both practising teachers and those in pre-service training.

Many of the earlier sections of this review have made reference to teachers' knowledge of the subject-matter. For example, developing understanding using a constructivist approach depends on the teacher recognising misconceptions and knowing the scientific view in order to help pupils towards it. Again, assessment by teachers is more accurate when they understand the subject themselves and such teachers encourage pupils' questions more than teachers with insecure background knowledge. There can be little room for doubt that in order to be effective in all aspects of teaching science, a sound understanding of the subject is necessary. That said, it is essential to add that this knowledge has to be integrated with other knowledge that teachers need.

Shulman (1987) provided a list of kinds of knowledge required to teach science, which, although often quoted, is worth recalling at this point:

- content knowledge – about science and of science
- general pedagogical knowledge – about classroom management and organisation that transcends subject matter
- curriculum knowledge – the guidelines, national requirements and materials available

- pedagogical content knowledge – about how to teach the subject matter, including useful illustrations, powerful analogies and examples
- knowledge of learners and their characteristics
- knowledge of educational contexts
- knowledge of educational goals, values and purposes, including the history and philosophy of education.

This list is a reminder that teachers need to know about pupils' thinking and reasoning, what kinds of preconceptions they are likely to have formed and what teacher interventions might bring about change towards a more scientific view. However it is significant that Shulman puts content knowledge first in this list, since several of the subsequent items depend on it. But what he emphasises is not so much the mastery of each and every aspect of a subject, as an understanding of what it is that identifies science; how the discipline of science differs from other disciplines; what are its boundaries, its limitations and the different ways in which it can be conceived. With this grasp, teachers can develop pedagogical content knowledge which he characterises as building 'bridges between their own understanding of the subject matter and the understanding that grows and is constructed in the minds of students' (Shulman, 1991). In this process, Shulman argues the central role of the use of analogies and metaphors and claims that 'the fundamental reasoning processes are analogical, not deductively logical'. But he recognises that analogies may not change pupils' ways of making sense of phenomena unless the teacher also takes account of pupils' preconceptions. It is helpful to have these points in mind in considering the research and views described in this part of the review.

The nature of teachers' misunderstandings

Although there was plenty of evidence prior to 1990 that primary teachers lacked confidence in teaching science, since that time that there has been a considerable increase in research in this area, prompted by the explicit statement in various national guidelines, curricula and standards, in the UK and elsewhere, of what has to be taught. As in the case of similar studies of pupils' understanding, many of these studies have had a focus on a specific concept area, such as force (Kruger *et al* 1990), energy (Summers and Kruger, 1992; Summers and Kruger, 1993), changes in materials (Kruger and Summers, 1989), gravity on the Moon (Noce *et al*, 1988), gravity and air resistance (Smith and Peacock, 1992), electric current (Webb, 1992), astronomy (Jones, 1991; Mant and Summers, 1993, Summers and Mant, 1995a), phases of the Moon (Targan, 1987) and the greenhouse effect (Boyes and Stanisstreet, 1993). The general finding across all these studies, carried out not only in the UK but in the US, Australia, South Africa and Italy has been that the explanations which many primary teachers could give of the concepts were at best incomplete and in many cases showed the same misconceptions as have been found to be held by secondary school students. Perhaps these findings are not all that surprising for two reasons. First, that primary teachers are recruited, by and large, from those for whom science was not a strength in their own achievement at school and their experience in the intervening time has done little to increase their achievement in this area. Second, that the methods used to assess teachers' knowledge of science were similar to those used with school students, complete with their association with previous failure and frustration.

Pre-service teachers

Research in the US with pre-service elementary school teachers (Kapuscinski, 1996) confirms the negative attitudes towards science held by female teachers in training. Given the high proportion of female primary teachers (92% in Scotland), it is important to address the particular feelings of women towards science and science teaching. Kapuscinski reports trainee teachers speaking of 'fear' 'nervousness', 'intimidation' in relation to science. Attitudes to science teaching were categorised as positive for only 12 out of 29 students studied. Reasons given for these feelings included not having any experience in their own education of hands-on activities, being taught from a text-book, being bored in science lessons, being tested by formal tests and receiving the implicit message that science is complicated and difficult.

During their course, with the opportunity to practise teaching science, the trainee teachers became more positive about teaching science. The research identified three main factors in this change of attitude. The most important was increased knowledge of how to teach and the realisation that there were many materials and resources to help them. In particular they valued the help available on video-disc and other technologies. Most described themselves as 'computer illiterate' but managed to overcome their inhibitions to become virtual technophiles. Opportunities to teach also helped to change attitudes as they developed general teaching skills. The realisation that they could meet, and enjoy, the challenge of teaching science was a further factor in developing more positive attitudes.

Vitale and Romance (1992) also used video-disc technology to improve pre-service elementary teachers' understanding of concepts in physical and earth science. Gains in scores in a test of science knowledge during a one-semester course were significantly greater than those of a comparable group not using the video-disc. The experimental group also showed significantly greater improvement in attitudes towards science teaching. Similar findings were reported by Appleton (1992) in Australia, working with pre-service teachers.

The importance of assessing changes in knowledge as well as in attitudes and confidence is underlined by research in Scotland. Gooday *et al* (1993) administered a questionnaire to first and fourth year BEd students, asking them, inter alia, to rate each item in a list of various scientific concepts in terms of their own understanding, their ability to explain it to children and its importance for children. The questionnaire also asked about the student teachers' confidence in teaching science and technology, about their attitudes to science and technology and about their own understanding of certain scientific ideas. The results showed that, compared with the first year students, the fourth year students were considerably more confident in teaching science, were more knowledgeable about classroom resources and how to use them and had greater understanding of science processes. At the same time the understanding of basic science concepts was little different in the first and fourth year students. It could be inferred from these results that the development of pedagogic skill and the experience of practising in the classroom had increased confidence in teaching science, despite little change in personal knowledge. As Gooday *et al* comment, it is necessary to question, 'whether the confidence of the fourth year students is relatively misplaced in the light of their generally poor understanding of a range of scientific concepts'. It also reminds us that there may be a considerable difference between self-expressed confidence and actual competence, a point borne out by research (Carré and Carter, 1993).

Serving teachers

The research of Bennett, Wragg, Carré and Carter at the University of Exeter underlines the view that the issue of background knowledge in primary teaching is more complex than whether or not the teachers have certain concepts (Wragg *et al*, 1989; Carré and Carter, 1990). They asked a random sample of over 900 teachers in England about how competent they felt to teach various subjects of the National Curriculum in 1989 just after the National Curriculum had been introduced. Science was ranked eighth out of ten subjects, with technology as tenth in terms of teachers' feeling of competence in teaching. In a follow-up survey in 1991 of over 400 teachers, technology remained at tenth but science had risen to the third place after English and mathematics. The researchers ascribed the significant positive change in the teachers' perceptions of their own competence in science to the allocation of resources, both human and material, to science teaching, together with the comprehensive map of the subject set out in the statutory orders (Bennett *et al*, 1992; Carré and Carter, 1993). Thus it seems plausible that gains in curriculum knowledge, pedagogic content knowledge and knowledge of goals, may have been responsible for the increase in confidence rather than increased personal understanding of science.

Relationship between confidence and understanding

Research carried out in Scotland over a period of two years into primary teachers' understanding of concepts in science and technology, provided information about the relationships between teachers' confidence in teaching science, their understanding of a range of key ideas and their background of science in their own education (Harlen, Holroyd and Byrne, 1995). Data were collected by questionnaire from a random sample of 514 primary teachers, about their background in science and their confidence in various aspects of teaching science and technology. Interviews were completed with a subset of 55 teachers taking part in the survey, in which their understanding of ideas in science and technology were probed. Subsequently 33 of these teachers kept notes about their teaching during a period of ten weeks and were interviewed about this work by telephone.

The results from the questionnaire survey confirmed findings of the previous survey in England by Wragg *et al* (1989), that primary teachers have very much less confidence in the knowledge and skills in teaching science, information technology and technology than they have in teaching English and mathematics. It is relevant to note that in the Scottish study 20 teachers only (ie 4% of the total) had a degree containing a science subject and for 18 of these the subject was a biological science. Only two teachers in the sample had a degree which included a pass in a physical science subject. Eighty-eight teachers had at least one Higher grade pass in a science subject and a further 90 teachers claimed at least one science subject pass at Ordinary ('O') grade, or its later replacement, Standard ('S') grade. Three hundred and fourteen teachers (61%) said they had *no* science qualifications.

For 55 teachers there was information about their background in science, their confidence in teaching and their understanding enabling the relationships between these variables to be explored. Using information about the extent of their understanding at the end of the interview, teachers were identified as being in the top one-third or bottom one-third of the group. The top 18 and the bottom 18 teachers were not significantly different in the length of their teaching experience – and not significantly different from the sample of teachers as a whole. Those rated in the top third for science understanding were more likely to have had some science in their background than not; but there was *no-one* in the bottom third who had some science in their background.

When confidence was added into the analysis it was found that there were teachers with no science in their background who were confident about teaching science, but whose understanding of science ideas was limited. In other words, it was possible for confidence to be somewhat misplaced. It is relevant to note that the male teachers expressed significantly more confidence than the female teachers although they had no science in their background beyond 'O' grade. At the same time there were teachers with no science in their background, but who had achieved understanding of key science ideas and whose confidence was low. In these cases they may have lacked knowledge of how to help children's understanding of these ideas. Finally, there were teachers with no science, low confidence and little understanding. There were a significant number of teachers like this and the findings derived from the discussion of their actual classroom work, carried out with the teachers by telephone, threw light on a puzzling finding, that many of them claimed not to find great difficulty in teaching science. What emerged was a series of strategies that teachers used to cope with low confidence in their ability to teach science. These included:

- avoidance – teaching as little of the subject as possible
- keeping to topics where their confidence was greater – usually meaning more biology than physical science
- stressing process outcomes rather than conceptual development outcomes
- relying on a book, or prescriptive work cards which give pupils step-by-step instructions
- emphasising expository teaching and underplaying questioning and discussion
- avoiding all but the simplest practical work and any equipment that could go wrong.

Teaching characterised by these features may enable teachers to include science in their planning and practice without constantly being faced with their own limitations in this area. Within this restricted practice then, it is possible that teachers may claim not to find teaching science particularly difficult. Furthermore if they retain a view of primary science, widely prevalent in Scottish primary schools in the 1980s, in which process is all and content does not matter, then they do not concern themselves with the development of pupils' understanding when evaluating their own success.

An optimistic outcome of this research was the response of teachers to being given the opportunity, in the individual interviews, discuss ideas and test out their own preconceptions. The relative ease with which understanding of some 'big ideas' was developed by the teachers suggested that there was latent understanding waiting to be awakened. This did not apply to all of the ideas discussed nor to all of the teachers, but it was sufficiently common to suggest that what holds back teachers' understanding is not *ability* to grasp ideas but the *opportunity* to discuss and develop them. At the same time, research of this kind, particularly if extended to cover the full range of 'big ideas' appropriate to primary education, can help in-service training to be targeted on those areas where teachers' understanding is most difficult to develop.

Classroom practice and teachers' understanding

Corroboration of the findings of the Scottish project about classroom activities came from a project in which direct classroom observations of practice were carried out, rather than relying on teachers reporting their classroom work. Osborne and Simon observed in six primary school classrooms as part of the ESRC-funded Mathematics and Science Task Project. Observations of teaching were supplemented by interviews with the teachers and some pupils. In one report (1996) they compared the teaching of two teachers who were both teaching the topic of light to eight-year-olds. These teachers had very different backgrounds in science: one (Fiona) had a science degree; the other (Carol) had a degree in languages. The researchers reported:

> Analysis of the classroom observations showed how the teachers' knowledge influenced their practice, including how tasks were selected for individual children, how children were questioned about light, and how the teachers responded to children's questions. (pp120–121)

In interviews with the pupils the researchers found that seven out of ten of Fiona's children were able to express a scientifically acceptable notion of how we see while not one of Carol's was able to provide this kind of answer. The researchers commented that the kinds of answers that were provided could have been predicted from the exchanges between pupils and their teacher in the classroom. Interviews with the teachers showed differences in their understanding of what they regarded as important for children's learning which led to the conclusion that the non-scientist was unable to judge what was the important idea that the pupils could develop from the activities. Carol was well aware of the limitation of her own knowledge and prevented its exposure by closing discussion of those aspects where she was uncertain.

Osborne and Simon (1996) drew some serious conclusions from this work, in particular, that too much is being asked of primary teachers by the demands of the National Curriculum in England:

> Essentially it would seem illogical to ask teachers to undertake extensive teaching of physical science when the overwhelming evidence, including our own, shows clearly that they often do not have the requisite skills to function effectively...The demands of the National Curriculum are simply beyond the capabilities and knowledge of the average primary teacher, who is likely to be female and the victim of a society that saw no value in education for women in any science other than biology. Such a view, with which we have considerable sympathy, does not argue that teachers should teach no science, but rather that the position where teachers are allowed to do more of those aspects of science in which they are confident, and less of those for which their confidence is low, is the only reasonable and just response. (p139)

Changing teachers' understandings

Other researchers, who have created and tried out ways of helping primary teachers to develop the necessary kinds of knowledge, have been more optimistic about the potential to change the present situation in primary school science. In particular, both in the US and the UK, constructivist approaches to learning have been applied to teacher education. In the UK, the Primary School Teachers and Science Project (PSTS, 1993) developed materials for use in both pre-service and in-service, which start from teachers' own understanding of science concepts. The materials were based on extensive earlier research into primary teachers' understanding of science concepts (Kruger *et al*, 1990; Summers and Kruger, 1992; Summers and Kruger, 1993; Kruger and Summers, 1989; Mant and Summers, 1993; Summers and Mant, 1995), which identified significant gaps in teachers' knowledge. The aims of the PSTS materials were to increase teachers' own understanding and to help them teach the concepts to pupils.

The PSTS work has been criticised by Golby *et al* (1995) and others (eg Osborne and Simon, 1996) for implying a deficiency model in relation to primary science teachers. Golby *et al* questioned the assumption that 'teachers need subject knowledge in order to impart it'. They pointed out that primary teachers' knowledge in almost any subject would be found to have flaws, but that in practice the necessary knowledge for teaching is obtained by working with colleagues and preparing themselves using other sources of information. In response, Mant and Summers (1995b) rejected the charge of assuming a 'transmission' model of teaching but reaffirmed that 'good subject matter knowledge is, in our view, an important prerequisite for good teaching, whatever the subject'. (p304)

Relevant in this context is work in the US by Stofflett (1994) who applied a constructivist approach to a ten week elementary teacher education programme to change views of trainee teachers about science teaching. The programme began with six sessions of activities which enabled the trainees to try out their ideas about a particular physical phenomenon, work towards the scientific view and then apply this in new contexts. The remaining fourteen sessions were spent in developing understanding of children's learning and conceptual change theory. Their reflection on their own conceptual change helped in applying these ideas in new areas. Research data were collected by interview, video-tapes and analysis of the trainees' practice teaching notes. These were analysed for evidence of change not only in relation to the understanding of science concepts but in conceptions of science teaching. Stofflett found positive changes which were evident in the lesson plans and field teaching. He acknowledged that these were found in a supportive environment and recognised that the less supportive climate of many schools may bring a reversion to less positive views of science teaching. He proposed that: 'To determine whether context-bound constraints (ie traditional schooling norms) induce dissatisfaction with newly formed conceptions, researchers should explore whether conceptual change pedagogy is fruitful over the long term. The two often clash'. (p807).

Teachers' conceptions of teaching and learning, as well as their confidence, was investigated by Aubusson and Webb (1992) in New South Wales, Australia. They evaluated the impact on forty teachers of a programme of professional development comprising two residential blocks separated by ten weeks. Evidence was collected by questionnaire before and after the programme and by participants interviewing each other about their views of teaching and learning, recording this in their journals which were analysed by the researchers. From the questionnaires it was found that the confidence to teach science increased significantly from the start to end of the course. Their responses to a question about what is important in science and technology education showed no change, however, and it was notable that knowledge was rated the lowest out of twelve items. Aubusson and Webb comment on this point that there was evidence from other parts of the study that:

> one of the reasons teachers fail to teach science and technology is because they perceive they lack the necessary scientific and technological knowledge. It is tempting to suggest that by rating the development of science and technology knowledge by pupils as relatively unimportant their own lack of knowledge becomes unimportant and their self-esteem as teachers is thereby protected. (p23)

From the analysis of the journals, Aubusson and Webb identified a number of factors which teachers put forward as reasons for not teaching in a way that they believed they ought to teach. They embraced, in theory, a child-centred approach but perceived factors which inhibited implementation as being time, pressure from supervisors, resources, child lacking necessary skills and formal testing. The researchers, however, noted that the teachers had no clear views on how to interact with pupils in order to promote learning; they lacked teaching strategies to translate their beliefs into practice. They suggested that these might be more a important factors than the perceived external influences.

The role of teachers' subject knowledge

These studies lead to the conclusion that, although the research leaves little room for doubt that increasing teachers' own understanding is a key factor in improving the quality of teaching and learning in science, there are other factors which have to be taken into account. There are strong arguments to support the view that the reason why understanding is needed is not so that teachers can convey factual information didactically to pupils. Rather it is so that they can ask questions that lead children to reveal and reflect on their ideas, so that they can avoid 'blind alleys', so that they can provide relevant sources of information and other resources, so that they can identify progress and the next steps that will take their learning further. These things cannot be done if teachers do not understand the ideas they are aiming for but what they need are the 'big ideas', the broad understanding that will enable them to guide children's learning. The aim cannot be to enable teachers to know the answers to all the questions children may ask. This would not only be impossible, given the creative curiosity of young children, but often inadvisable when children would not understand the answer. What teachers need to have at their fingertips are strategies for *handling* children's questions and turning them to the advantage of investigative learning. They also need sources of information and a level of general understanding that facilitates quick and effective use of these sources. Again, this points to the need for understanding of broad principles, the 'big ideas', that enables use of their professional skills (Harlen, 1998).

Some conclusions about teachers' understanding

- The low level of confidence about teaching science and of understanding of science concepts has been well established by research conducted in many countries.

- The impact of teachers' confidence and understanding on pupils' learning opportunities has also been established by research, low levels of confidence and understanding being associated with restricting classroom activities to following instructions and inhibiting creativity and questioning.

- There is disagreement as to the appropriate action that would improve pupils' classroom experiences; in particular about the feasibility of the curriculum demands and of providing sufficient continuing professional development for teachers.

- The use of computers and multimedia aids can have an important role in improving primary science teaching.

10

Discussion

This review has covered a number of aspects of science education that have impact on students' achievement, but by no means all. A notable omission is the matter of gender and attainment which has attracted a vast amount of research in all countries and over many years. Omission here is justified by the publication of recent reviews which have synthesised research on differential achievement (Powney, 1996; Arnot *et al*, 1998) and on classroom processes (Howe, 1997). In relation to the aspects which have been covered here, it is useful to bring together the summary conclusions for each section before drawing out the themes which cut across them.

Conclusions
Practical work

- Practical work should be seen as a means to various ends and not as an end in itself.
- The learning that is intended from a particular piece of practical work should be clear and it should to be tailored in order that it can serve that purpose effectively.
- Both teachers and pupils need to be aware of the purpose of the practical work in a particular case and prepare for it and follow it up in relation to the specific purpose.
- There are three main purposes for practical work which have emerged from this review:
  - Providing first-hand experience, so that pupils can 'see it for themselves' and in some cases do it themselves, although this purpose is often best served by a good demonstration or a field trip rather than 'hands on' practical work.
  - Testing ideas by making predictions, setting up a valid test, collecting reliable evidence and relating what is found to the original idea. This practical work should be theory-based.

- Experience of 'doing science' through carrying out an investigation which has a degree of open-endedness.

Using computers

- Science education can benefit from the use of computers for all kinds of applications and for delivering ICT.

- Data-logging and graphing can save time and increase pupils' focus on the meaning of results from practical work rather than on the process of gathering data and drawing graphs. These benefits are found particularly with first and second year secondary pupils and less able pupils.

- Simulations, in combination with practical work, can be effective in helping pupils' to change non-scientific conceptions, when they are designed to address these preconceptions, although not all are eliminated.

- Simulations have potential disadvantages in projecting a misleading notion of reality.

- Modelling by students can be helped by computer programs but the teacher's role remains a central one for promoting recognition of false assumptions and encouraging reflection.

- The Internet offers many opportunities, yet to be fully exploited and researched, for both pupils and teachers.

- The use of interactive multimedia has considerable potential to link different representations and ways of learning to develop understanding in science. However the effective use of this technology makes no less demand on teachers' understanding than conventional classroom activities.

Constructivism

- There is a very sound base of evidence for the existence in pupils of their own constructions about scientific phenomena in the world around, even before they have been exposed to relevant teaching.

- These ideas make sense to the pupils because they are based on everyday experience; but they are also formed through 'everyday' thinking and they often conflict with the scientific view.

- Learning is seen as changing pupils' own ideas into ones consistent with the scientific view.

- Approaches to changing pupils' ideas all begin with some activities which are designed so that pupils express their ideas and make them available to the teacher.

- There is less consensus about how to introduce the scientific view. Approaches vary from facing pupils with a discrepant event, conflicting with their view, to using the pupils' view as a basis for a prediction and testing its validity.

- The arguments of Vygotsky suggest that the teacher has an important role in assisting development and taking the learner further than he or she might be able to go unassisted.

- There is no firm evidence of the effectiveness of different approaches to developing pupils ideas within a constructivist framework.

Cognitive acceleration

- The Cognitive Acceleration in Science Education (CASE) is a programme of interventions designed to develop formal operational thinking.

- The effect of CASE activities on performance has been thoroughly investigated, more so than for many other types of intervention.

- Long-term effects have been shown in terms of raised achievement in mathematics and English as well as in science.

- There is no suggestion that CASE-type work should replace teaching of content in science but as a supplement there is evidence that it can have beneficial effects.

- Its success depends on the teachers undergoing special training.

- Certain aspects of the CASE approach, particularly metacognition and linking thinking strategies to problems in different contexts, find support from other studies of effective teaching where they appear to be among the key factors.

Assessment

- This part of the review has focused on formative assessment, that is, assessment designed to assist teaching and learning.

- There is evidence that improving formative assessment can raise standards in a wide range of different learning contexts.

- Assessment is only formative when it reflects the aims of learning and is used in making decisions about the next steps in learning.

- Current practice lacks many of the features which research shows are central to a positive impact on achievement.
- Feedback to pupils is important so that they can take part in deciding how to improve their performance and should be of the form which makes this possible.
- Effective feedback focuses on the work and does not make judgements about the ability of the pupil or comparisons with other pupils.
- Planning what is to be assessed and how to do it is an important part of teachers' preparation.
- There is need for further research on the effectiveness of published assessment materials.

Planning, questioning and using language

- Pupils' learning is supported most effectively when teachers have planned lessons carefully towards the development of identified skills and understanding, that is, when they know what they want pupils to learn.
- Teachers may make too few demands on higher level thinking in lower secondary classes in response to pupils' reactions; it is easier to keep pupils on task when the cognitive demand is lower.
- Greater demands on pupils have to be matched by effective monitoring in classrooms to ensure pupils' engagement with tasks, to encourage and answer their questions and to support their development of understanding.
- Opportunities for pupils to raise questions provides teachers with access to pupils' ideas; higher achievements are associated with pupils asking strategic questions.
- Teachers' questions which are open and demand higher level of thinking encourage higher achievement in pupils.
- Teachers' planning should focus on what teachers will do and what pupils are intended to learn as well as on what pupils will do.
- When pupils work in groups the evidence suggests that learning is increased when tasks are structured to promote collaboration and are followed by whole class discussion.
- Pupils need help as well as opportunity to write about their findings and ideas in their own word.

- Non-technical words used in the context of science can be as confusing as technical words and teachers need to ensure that pupils share their understanding of the vocabulary used.

The curriculum

- Attention should be given to the complexity of the reasoning which is demanded for understanding when placing the study of various phenomena within the curriculum framework.
- There is evidence that some ideas common across science are more easily developed in some content areas than others and their generalisation should not be assumed.
- Research evidence about the conceptual development of pupils should be used in planning and sequencing curriculum guidelines.
- Understanding and confidence in teaching science appears to be an important factor in effective teaching of environmental education.

Teachers' understanding of science

- The low level of confidence about teaching science and of understanding of science concepts has been well established by research conducted in many countries.
- The impact of teachers' confidence and understanding on pupils' learning opportunities has also been established by research, low levels of confidence and understanding being associated with restricting classroom activities to following instructions and inhibiting creativity and questioning.
- There is disagreement as to the appropriate action that would improve pupils' classroom experiences; in particular about the feasibility of the curriculum demands and of providing sufficient continuing professional development for teachers.
- The use of computers and multimedia aids can have an important role in improving primary science teaching.

Discussion

Several themes emerge for consideration in any revision of practice in science teaching: practical work; the use of computers; increased emphasis on reflection and meta-cognition; assessment; questioning; planning; and improving teachers' understanding of science and of teaching and learning science.

It appears that practical work often fails to serve a useful purpose and sometimes may inhibit more than help understanding. Good demonstrations or computer-based simulations can help pupils' understanding, where that is the purpose, more effectively than time-consuming benchwork. This is not to say by any means that there is no role for practical work, only that it should be used selectively and where it is best suited to the purpose. In particular, practical work has important functions, in which it can be assisted by, but not replaced by, demonstrations or computer programs. These are enabling pupils: to see a phenomenon or effect for themselves; to decide what to change and then try it in order to test a theory or their own ideas; to conduct an open-ended investigation, using the full range of physical and mental process skills; and to gain some understanding of the nature and limitations of scientific knowledge and procedures.

The use of computers emerges as an increasingly important aspect of classroom practice and teacher education. Users enjoy working with computers and find they help understanding. Multimedia programs have a particular role in linking ideas across different contexts and encouraging application of concepts by pupils. However, there is a health warning that computer programs can give a false sense of what is reality and of what can be accomplished through scientific investigation. A judicious mixture of simulation and real experience is essential to avoid this.

Using computers for data-logging and graphing enhances practical work and allows pupils to focus on trends and relationships rather than the collection of individual items of data. Taking the drudgery out of practical work saves time which can be used to investigate other values of variables or other variables to test predictions. However it is important to note that these benefits depend on the pupils making efforts to interpret and try to explain their findings. Studies have shown that such efforts are more likely to be made when the teacher directs their attention and probes thinking with question which provoke prediction and hypothesising.

In all the discussion of practical work, it is important not to lose sight of the essential purpose – to bring about pupils' learning in science. The research on learning confirms the foundation of evidence on which constructivism is based; that learners bring pre-existing ideas to new experience and that if these are non-scientific they are often difficult to change. The question to which there seems, as yet, no 'tried and tested' answer however, is: how should the teacher ensure that the pupils come to understand the scientific view? Researchers have observed that pupils have to find the alternatives to their own ideas to be more useful, more plausible and more fruitful before they will genuinely embrace them and relinquish their own ideas. The process of bringing about change in ideas takes longer than is often allowed for in curriculum planning and so we should make sure that time is spent on the 'big' ideas and the ones that will lay a foundation for scientific literacy.

An approach to assisting pupils' learning by focusing on the development of thinking skills has been shown to have a long-term effect in raising achievement. The cognitive acceleration in science education (CASE) programme encourages pupils to pay attention to variables and their manipulation and to reflect on their thinking. The significance of such meta-cognition is also regarded by other researchers in this field as central to learning and occurs in the descriptions of the practice of effective teachers. It is related to engaging pupils as partners in their own learning, through encouraging reflection on how they use evidence in coming to conclusions, how they solve problems and so helping them to begin to identify their own learning processes.

The involvement of pupils is also part of the messages about assessment which emerges as a theme across the evidence. The formative use of assessment is invariably found in effective teaching and it has a potentially large impact on achievement. For this impact to be realised, however, teachers need to know the lines of progression in learning and use the information from assessment to decide, in collaboration with the pupils where appropriate, the next steps in learning. The use of the information in furthering learning is assisted by pupils being involved in the process throughout and gradually being able to apply the criteria used by their teacher in assessing their work for themselves and deciding what needs to be done to improve it.

For teachers to recognise lines of progression, as effective formative assessment requires, depends in large part on the progression being evident in the curriculum guidelines and teaching materials. Researchers in the field of pupils' learning claim that enough is now known about the course of conceptual development, from cross-age studies, for this information to be used in the formulation of curricula. Such application would help to avoid teachers spending time attempting to develop understanding of ideas that are too difficult for pupils, or, worse, leaving such ideas half-formed and giving pupils a sense that science is too complex for them to understand.

Other aspects of effective teaching cluster round the notion of good planning and monitoring the implementation of plans. Features of good lesson planning involve attention to what the teacher will do and say as well as to what pupils will do. This includes thinking beforehand about questions to ask pupils that will require use of higher level thinking skills, structuring group work to promote collaboration and discussion, encouraging pupils to ask questions and planning reporting and writing tasks which provoke reflection in pupils.

Much evidence has emerged of teachers making too little demand of pupils. In many cases, and particularly in primary classes, the cause is the teacher's poor knowledge of the subject matter and associated lack of confidence. However, there is also evidence that the appropriate response may be to support teachers in the ways they plan lessons, integrating information about subject matter with information about how to teach it. There is evidence of increasing and successful use of information technology to help in this process. Combined with developments in the use of computers in the classroom by pupils, there is potential for using this technology to improve the level of understanding of science education by teachers and the level of achievement of pupils in learning science.

Reviewing existing research has several functions, among which are showing what are possible options for change and what is known about the consequences of adopting these options. This review has pointed to some actions that are likely to improve the opportunities for learning science of 9 to 14-year-olds in Scotland and elsewhere.

Whilst some changes can certainly not be undertaken in a short time-scale – for example, raising the level of knowledge and understanding in science of primary teachers – nevertheless, knowing the extent that this is important informs decisions about starting the processes necessary to improve this situation in the long run. Rather more readily implemented are matters relating to the formative use of assessment, practical work and the use of computers. The relatively better performance in international surveys of Scottish pupils in practical work as compared with written tests may suggest that there is room to reconsider the balance of time spent on laboratory work compared with other work or at least to ensure that practical work is assisting understanding as well as the acquisition of practical skills. Using computers to reduce the time spent in repetitive data collection could free more time for thinking and reflecting on the meaning of evidence gathered. There is also evidence that time spent in 'thinking about thinking' may have far-reaching effects on achievement.

Reviews also serve the purpose of revealing what is not known and where further research is needed. Here the lack of systematic study has been particularly evident in relation to the effectiveness of different approaches to developing students' ideas in constructivist methodologies. There is also a dearth of studies of how to prepare teachers who have not only the skills and knowledge they need for teaching, but the extra commitment and enthusiasm for science that in turn creates enthusiastic and willing students.

References

Adams, S. (1991) All in the mind. *School Science Review*, 72: 9–103.

Adey, P. (1988) Cognitive acceleration – review and prospects. *International Journal of Science Education* , 10 (2): 121–34.

Adey, P. (1997) It all depends on the context, doesn't it? Searching for general, educable dragons. *Studies in Science Education*, 29: 45–92.

Adey, P. & Shayer, M. (1990) Accelerating the development of formal thinking in middle and high school students. *Journal of Research in Science Teaching*, 27 (3): 267–285.

Adey, P. & Shayer, M. (1993) An exploration of long-term far-transfer effects following an extended intervention programme in the high-school science curriculum. *Cognition and Instruction*, 11 (1): 1–29.

Adey, P., Shayer, M. & Yates, C. (1989) *Thinking Science: the Curriculum Materials of the CASE Project*. London: Nelson.

Alton-Lee, A., Nuthall, G. & Patrick, J. (1993) Reframing classroom research: a lesson from the private world of children. *Harvard Educational Review*, 63 (1): 50–84.

Applebee, A.N. (1984) Writing and reasoning. *Review of Educational Research*, 54: 577–596.

Appleton, K. (1992) Discipline knowledge and confidence to teach science: self-perceptions of primary teacher education students. *Research in Science Education*, 22: 11–19.

APU (1986) *Science in Schools, Age 13. A Report for Teachers*. London: Department of Education and Science.

Arnot, M., Gray, J., James, J. with Duveen, G. (1988) *Recent Research on Gender and Educational Performance*. London: OFSTED.

Aubusson, P. & Webb, C. (1992) Teacher beliefs about learning and teaching in primary science and technology. *Research in Science Education*, 22: 20–29.

Baird, J.R. & Mitchell, I. (Eds) (1986) *Improving the Quality of Teaching and Learning: an Australian Case Study. The PEEL project*. Melbourne: Monash University.

Bangert-Drowns, R.L., Kulik C.-L. & Kulik, J.A. (1985) Effectiveness of computer-based instruction in secondary schools. *Journal of Computer-based Instruction*, 12: 59–68.

Bangert-Drowns, R.L. Kulik, C.-L., Kulik, J.A. & Morgan, M.T. (1991) Effects of frequent classroom testing. *Journal of Educational Research*, 85: 89–99.

Barnes, D. (1976) *From Communication to Curriculum*. Harmondsworth: Penguin.

Barton, R. (1997) How do computers affect graphical interpretation? *School Science Review*, 79 (287): 55–60.

Beatty, J.W. & Woolnough, B.E. (1982) Practical work in 11–13 science. *British Educational Research Journal*, 8: 23–30.

Bennett, S.N., Wragg, E.C., Carré, C.G. & Carter, D.S.G. (1992) A longitudinal study of primary teachers' perceived competence in, and concerns about, National Curriculum implementation. *Research Papers in Education*, 7 (1): 53–78.

Benson, A. (1986) *Children's Understanding of Science in Four Comprehensive Schools*. Unpublished MEd thesis, University of Manchester.

Bishop, K. & Denley, P. (1997) The fundamental role of subject matter knowledge in the teaching of science. *School Science Review*, 79 (286): 65–71.

Black, H. (1986) Assessment for learning. In: Nuttall, D. (Ed) *Assessing Educational Achievement*. London: Falmer Press.

Black, P.J. (1993) Formative and summative assessment by teachers. *Studies in Science Education*, 21: 49–97.

Black, P.J. & Wiliam, D. (1998a) *Inside the Black Box: Raising standards through classroom assessment*. King's College, London.

Black, P.J. & Wiliam, D. (1998b) Assessment and classroom learning. *Assessment in Education*, 5 (1): 7–74.

Bliss, J. (1995) Piaget and after: the case of learning science. *Studies in Science Education*, 25:139–172.

Blissett, G. & Atkins, M. (1993) Are they thinking? A study of the use of interactive video. *Computers and Education*, 21 (1): 31–39.

Bottrill, J. & Lock, R. (1993) Do students learn from pictures or from text? *Science Review*, 74:109–112.

Boyes, E. & Stanisstreet, M. (1993) The 'Greenhouse Effect': children's perceptions of causes, consequences and cures. *International Journal of Science Education,* 15 (5): 531–552.

Butler, R. (1987) Task-involving and ego-involving properties of evaluation: effects of different feedback conditions on motivational perceptions, interest and performance. *Journal of Educational Psychology,* 79: 236–243.

Carey, S., Evans, R., Honda, M., Jay, E. & Under, C. (1989) An experiment is when you try to see if it works: a case study of grade 7 students' understanding of the construction of scientific knowledge. *International Journal of Science Education,* 11: 514–529.

Carlsen, W.S. (1987) Questioning in classrooms – a sociological perspective. *Review of Educational Research,* 61:157–178.

Carré, C. & Carter, D. (1990) Primary teachers' self-perceptions concerning implementation of the national curriculum for science in the UK. *International Journal of Science Education,* 12 (4): 327–431.

Carré, C. & Carter, D. (1993) Primary teachers' self-perceptions concerning implementation of the national curriculum for science in the UK – revisited. *International Journal of Science Education,* 15 (4): 457–470.

Carson, S.R. (1997) The use of spreadsheets in science – an overview. *School Science Review,* 79 (287): 69–80.

Champagne, A.B., Klopfer, L. & Gunstone, R.F. (1982) Cognitive research and the design of science instruction. *Educational Psychologist,* 12: 31–53.

Claxton, G. (1993) Mini-theories: a preliminary model for learning science. In: Black, P.J. & Lucas, A.M. (Eds) *Children's Informal Ideas in Science.* London: Routledge.

Clough, D. (1987) Word processing in the classroom and science education. *Primary Science Review,* (5) 5.

Crooks, T.J. (1988) The impact of classroom evaluation practices on students. *Review of Educational Research.* 58 (4): 438–481.

Diffey, I. (1997) The use of an intranet in school science. *School Science Review,* 79 (287): 28.

Donaldson, M. (1978) *Children's Mind.* Glasgow: Fontana.

Driver, R. (1983) *The Pupil as Scientist?* Milton Keynes: Open University Press.

Driver, R. & Bell, B. (1986) Students' thinking and the learning of science: a constructivist view. *School Science Review*, 67: 443–456.

Driver, R. & Easley, J. (1978) Pupils and paradigms: a review of literature related to concept development in adolescent science students. *Studies in Science Education* (5): 61–84.

Driver, R. & Erikson, G. (1983) Theories-in-action: some theoretical and empirical issues in the study of students' conceptual frameworks in science. *Studies in Science Education*, (10): 37–60.

Driver, R. & Oldham, V. (1986) A constructivist approach to curriculum development in science. *Studies in Science Education*, (13): 105–122.

Driver, R., Leach, J., Scott, P. & Wood-Robinson, C. (1994) Young people's understanding of science concepts: implications of cross-age studies for curriculum planning. *Studies in Science Education*, (24): 75–100.

Ehindero, O.J. (1985) Differential cognitive responses to adjunct study questions in the learning of chemistry textual materials. *European Journal of Science Education*, 7 (4): 423–430.

Erikson, G. (1970) Children's conceptions of heat and temperature. *Science Education*, 63: 221–230.

Fawns, R. & Sadler, J. (1996) Managing students' learning in classrooms: reframing classroom research. *Research in Science Education*, 26 (2): 205–217.

Fensham, P.J. & Kass, H. (1988) Inconsistent and discrepant events in science instruction. *Studies in Science Education*, (15): 1–16.

Feuerstein, R., Rand, Y., Hoffman, M. & Miller, M. (1980) *Instrumental Enrichment: An Intervention Programme for Cognitive Modifiability*. Baltimore: University Park Press.

Gallagher, J.J. & Tobin, K. (1987) Teacher management and student engagement in high school science. *Science Education*, (71): 535–55.

Galton, M.J., Simon, B. & Croll, P. (1980) *Inside the Primary Classroom*. London: Routledge.

Gardner, P.L. (1972) *Words in Science*. Australian Science Education Project.

Gardner, P. & Gauld, C. (1990) Labwork and students' attitudes. In: Hegarty-Hazel, E. (Ed) *The Student Laboratory and the Science Curriculum*. London: Routledge.

Garrett, R.M. & Roberts, I.F. (1982) Demonstration versus small group practical work in science education. A critical review of studies since 1900. *Studies in Science Education*, (9):109–146.

Garnett, P.J. & Tobin, K. (1988) Teaching for understanding: exemplary practice in high school chemistry. *Journal of Research in Science Teaching*, 26 (1): 1–14.

Gauld, C. (1984) Empirical evidence and conceptual change. In: Osborne, R. & Gilbert, J. (Eds) *Some Issues of Theory in Science Education*. University of Waikato (New Zealand).

Gauld, C. & Hukins, A.A. (1980) Scientific attitudes: a review. *Studies in Science Education*, 7:129–161.

Gayford, C. (1988) Aims, purposes and emphasis in practical biology at Advanced Level – a study of teachers' attitudes. *School Science Review*, (69): 799–802.

Gilbert, J. & Watts, M. (1983) Concepts, misconceptions and alternative conceptions: changing perspectives in science education. *Studies in Science Education*, (10): 37–60.

Golby, M., Martin, A. & Porter, M. (1995) Some researchers' understanding of primary teaching: comments on Mant and Summers' 'Some primary school teachers' understanding of the Earth's place in the universe'. *Research Papers in Education*, 10 (3): 297–302.

Gooday, M., Payne, F. & Wilson, J. (1993) *Primary student teachers' scientific knowledge and their attitudes towards science.* Northern College (Aberdeen and Dundee).

Goodfellow, T. (1990) Spreadsheets: powerful tools in science education. *School Science Review*, 71 (257): 47.

Gorman, T.P., White, J., Brooks, G., Maclure, M. & Kispal, A. (1988) *Language Performance in Schools: Review of APU Language Monitoring 1979–1983*. London: HMSO.

Gould, C.D. (1978) Practical work in sixth form biology. *Journal of Biological Education*, 12: 33–38.

Grosslight, L., Unger, C., Jay, E. & Smith, C.L. (1991). Understanding models and their uses in science: conceptions of middle and high school students and experts. *Journal of Research in Science Teaching*, (28): 799–822.

Gunstone, R.F. (1991) Reconstructing theory from practical experience. In: Woolnoough, B.E. (Ed) *Practical Science*. Milton Keynes: Open University Press.

Gunstone, R.F. & Champagne, A.B. (1990) Promoting conceptual change in the laboratory. In: Hegarty-Hazel, E. (Ed) *The Student Laboratory and the Science Curriculum*. London: Routledge.

Hall, S. (1997) The problem of differentiation. *School Science Review,* 78 (284): 95–98.

Harlen, W (1986) *Creativity and Rationality in Learning and Teaching Science*. Occasional Paper, University of Liverpool Department of Education.

Harlen, W. (1992) Research and development of science in the primary school. *International Journal of Science Education,* 14 (5): 491–503.

Harlen, W. (1995) Standards and science education in Scottish schools. *Studies in Science Education,* (26): 107–134.

Harlen, W. (1997) Criteria for identifying progression in scientific Ideas for Primary School Pupils. In: Harnqvist, K. & Burgen, A. (Eds) *Growing up with Science*. London: Jessica Kingsley.

Harlen, W., Holroyd, C. & Byrne, M. (1995) *Confidence and Understanding in Teaching Science and Technology in Primary Schools*. Edinburgh: Scottish Council for Research in Education.

Harlen, W. & Jelly, S.J. (1997) *Developing Primary Science*. London: Longman.

Harlen, W. & Schilling, M. (1998) *Evaluation of the Science On-Line Support Network (SOLSN) Feasibility Study*. Edinburgh: Scottish Office and Scottish Council for Research in Education.

Harris, S. (1998) International maths and science study. *Education Journal,* April, 24–26.

Hartley, J.R. (1994) Multimedia views of science education. *Studies in Science Education,* (23): 75–87.

Hein, G.F. (1991) Active assessment for active learning. In: Perrone, V. (Ed) *Expanding Students Assessment*. Alexandra, Virginia: Association of Supervision and Curriculum Development.

Henderson, J. (1994) Teaching sensitive issues in science: the case of sex education. In: Wellington, J.J. (Ed) *Secondary Science: Contemporary Issues and Practical Approaches*. London: Routledge.

Henderson, J. & Wellington, J. (1998) Lowering the language barrier in learning and teaching science. *School Science Review,* 79 (288): 35–46.

Hodson, D. (1990) A critical look at practical work in school science. *School Science Review,* (70): 33–40.

Hodson, D. (1992a) Assessment of practical work: some considerations in philosophy of science. *Science and Education,* (1): 115–144.

Hodson, D. (1992b) Redefining and reorienting practical work in school science. *School Science Review,* (73): 65–78.

Hodson, D. (1993) Re-thinking old ways: towards a more critical approach to practical work in school science. *Studies in Science Education,* (22): 85–142.

Hofstein, A. & Lunetta, V.N. (1982) The role of the laboratory in science teaching: neglected aspects of research. *Review of Educational Research,* (52): 201–217.

Holliday, W.G. & Benson, G. (1991) Enhancing learning using questions adjunct to science charts. *Journal of Research in Science Teaching,* 28 (6): 523–535.

Holliday, W.G. & McGuire, B. (1992) How can comprehension adjunct questions focus students' attention and enhance concept learning of a computer-animated science lesson? *Journal of Research in Science Teaching,* 29 (1): 3–16.

Holton, G. (1978) Subelectrons, presuppositions and the Millikan-Ehrenheft dispute. In: Holton, G. (Ed) *The Scientific Imagination: Case Studies.* Cambridge: Cambridge University Press.

Howe, C. (1997) *Gender and Classroom Interaction: A Research Review.* Edinburgh: The Scottish Council for Research in Education.

Jackson, R. & Bazley, M. (1997) Science education and the Internet – cutting through the hype. *School Science Review,* 79 (287): 41–44.

Jelly, S.J. (1985) Helping children to raise questions – and answering them. In: Harlen, W. (Ed) *Primary Science: Taking the Plunge.* London: Heinemann Educational Books.

Johnstone, A.H. (1984) New stars for the teacher to steer by? *Journal of Chemical Education,* 61: 847–849.

Johnstone, A.H. & Letton, K.M. (1990) Investigating undergraduate laboratory work. *Education in Chemistry,* (27): 9–11.

Johnstone, A.H. & Wham, A.J.B. (1982) The demands of practical work. *Education in Chemistry,* (19) 71–73.

Johnstone, A.H., Hogg, W., Macquire, P. & Raja, S. (1997) How long is a chain? Reasoning in science. *School Science Review,* 78 (285): 73–77.

Jones, B. (1991) *Pre-service elementary teachers' explanations of diurnal, seasonal and lunar phenomena.* School of Education: University of Tasmania.

Kapuscinski, P. (1996) *Factors Influencing Female Teachers' Attitudes Towards Science and Science Teaching.* Paper presented at the 16th Annual International Seminar for Teacher Education. Brazil, April.

Kerr, J.F. (1963) *Practical Work in School Science.* Leicester: Leicester University Press.

Krishner, P.A. (1992) Epistemology, practical work and academic skills in science education. *Science and Education,* (1): 273–299.

Kruger, C. (1992) Surveys of English primary teachers conceptions of force, energy and materials. *Science Education,* 76 (4): 339–351.

Kruger, C. & Summers, M. (1989) An investigation of some primary teachers' understanding of changes in materials. *School Science Review,* 71 (December), 17–27.

Kulik, C.-L. & Kulik, J.A. (1991) Effectiveness of computer-based instruction: an updated analysis. Computers in Human Behaviour, 7: 75–94.

Kruger, C., Palacio, D. & Summers, M. (1990) A survey of primary school teachers' conceptions of force and motion. *Educational Research,* (32): 83–95.

Langer, J.A. & Applebee, A.N. (1987) *How Writing Shapes Thinking: A Study of Teaching and Learning.* Urbana, Il: National Council of Teachers.

Laslett, A., Perkins, K., Weeks, B. & Comber, K. (1992) *Writing and Reading Assessment Program. Final Report: Summary.* Adelaide: Education Department of South Australia.

Latchem, C., Williamson, J. & Henderson-Lancett, L. (Eds) (1993) *Interactive Multimedia: Practice and Promise.* London: Kogan Page.

Leach, J. & Scott, P. (1995) The demands of learning science concepts – issues of theory and practice. *School Science Review,* 76 (277): 47–51.

Leach, J., Driver, R., Scott, P. & Wood-Robinson, C. (1994) Children's ideas about ecology. *International Journal of Science Education* (1), (2) and (3).

Lewis, E.L., Stern, J.L. & Linn, M. (1993) The effect of computer simulations on introductory thermodynamics understanding. *Educational Technology*, January, 45–58.

Lewis, M. & Wray D. (1996) *Writing Frames: Scaffolding Children's Non-Fiction Writing*. University of Reading: Reading and Language Information Centre.

Lewis, M. & Wray D. (1998) *Writing Across the Curriculum: Writing Frames to Support Learning*. University of Reading: Reading and Language Information Centre.

Littledyke, M. (1997) Science education for environmental education? Primary teacher perspectives and practices. *British Educational Research Journal*, 23 (5): 641–659.

Malcolm, H. & Schlapp, U. (1997) *5–14 in the Primary School: A Continuing Challenge*. Edinburgh: Scottish Council for Research in Education.

Mant, J. & Summers, M. (1993) Some primary school teachers' understanding of the Earth's place in the universe. *Research Papers in Education,* 8 (1): 101–129.

Martin, J.R. (1990) Literacy in science: learning how to handle text as technology. In: Christie, F. (Ed) *Literacy for a changing world*. Hawthorn, Victoria: ACER.

Millar, R. (1989) What is scientific methods and can it be taught? In: Wellington, J.J. (Ed) *Skills and Processes in Science Education*. London: Routledge.

Millar, R. & Kragh, W. (1994) Alternative frameworks or context-specific reasoning? Children's ideas about the motion of projectiles. *School Science Review*, 75 (272): 27–34.

Mitman, A.L., Mergendoller, J.R., Packer, M.J. & Marchman, V.A. (1984) *Secondary Science and Mathematics Improvement Program* (report). San Francisco: Far West Laboratory for Educational Research Development.

Newton, L. (1997) Graph talk: some observations and reflections on students' data-logging. *School Science Review*, 79 (287): 49–54.

Noce, G., Torosantucci, G. & Vicenti, V. (1988) The floating of objects on the Moon: prediction from a theory or experimental fact? *International Journal of Science Education,* (10): 61–70.

Nuffield Primary Science (1997) *Understanding Science Ideas: A Guide for Primary Teachers.* London: Collins Educational

Nunes, T., Shliemann, A. & Carraher, D. (1993*) Street mathematics and school mathematics.* Cambridge: Cambridge University Press.

Nussbaum, J. & Novick, S. (1981) Brainstorming in the classroom to invent a model: a case study. *School Science Review,* 62 (221): 771–778.

Nuthall, G.A. & Alton-Lee, A.G. (1992) Understanding how students learn in classrooms. In: Pressley, M., Harris, K. & Guthrie, J. (Eds) *Promoting Academic Competence and Literacy in School.* San Diego: Academic Press.

OECD / CERI (1997) *Education at a Glance. OECD Indicators.* Paris: Centre for Educational Research and Innovation.

Ogborn, J. (1990) A future for modelling in science education. *Journal of Computer Assisted Learning,* 6: 103–12.

Osborne, J. (1997) Practical alternatives. *School Science Review,* (78): 61–66.

Osborne, J. & Simon, S. (1996) Primary science: past and future directions. *Studies in Science Education,* (26) 99–147.

Osborne, R.J. & Freyberg, P. (1985*) Learning in Science: The implications of 'Children's Science'.* New Zealand: Heinemann.

O'Shea, T., Scanlon, E., Byard, M., Draper, S., Driver, R., Hennessy, S., Hartely, R., O'Malley, C., Mallen, C., Mohammed, G. & Twigger, D. (1993) Twenty-nine children, five computers and a teacher. In: Edwards, D., Scanlon, E. & West, R. (Eds) *Teaching, Learning and Assessment in Science Education.* London: Open University Press.

Palmer, D. (1997) Linking theory and practice: a strategy for presenting primary science activities. *School Science Review,* 79 (286): 73–80.

Perkins, D. & Saloman, G. (1989) Are cognitive skills context bound? *Educational Researcher,* 18 (1): 16–25.

Plowman, L. (1997) Getting side-tracked: cognitive overload, narrative, and interactive learning environments. In: O'Shea, T. (Ed) *Virtual Environments and the Role of the Teacher.* London: Open University Press.

Powney, J. (1996) *Gender and Attainment: A Review.* Edinburgh: The Scottish Council for Research in Education.

Primary School Teachers and Science (PSTS) Project (1991–93) *Understanding Forces, Understanding Energy, Understanding Living Things, Understanding Changes in Materials, Understanding the Earth's Place in the Universe.* Teacher Education Materials for Primary School Science. Oxford: Oxford University Department of Educational Studies and Westminster College Oxford.

Raghavan, K. & Glaser, R. (1995) Model-based analysis and reasoning in Science: the MARS curriculum. *Science Education,* 79 (1): 37–61.

Raizen, S.A., Baron, J.B., Champagne, A.B., Haertel, E., Mullis, I.V.S. & Oakes, J. (1989) *Assessment in Science Education: the Middle Years.* Washington: National Center for Improving Science Education.

Raizen, S.A., Baron, J.B., Champagne, A.B., Haertel, E., Mullis, I.V.S. & Oakes, J. (1990) *Assessment in Elementary School Science.* Washington: National Center for Improving Science Education.

Ratcliffe, M. (1998) Initial Teacher Education. *Education in Science,* 177: 8–9.

Resnick, L.B. (1987) *Education and Learning to Think.* Washington DC: National Academy Press.

Resnick, L.B. & Resnick, D.P. (1992) Assessing the thinking curriculum: new tools for educational reform. In: Gifford, B.R. & O'Connor, M.C. (Eds) *Changing Assessment: Alternative Views of Aptitude.* Boston: Kluwer.

Reynolds, A.J. (1991) Effects of an experiment-based physical science programme on cognitive outcomes. *Journal of Educational Research,* 84 (5): 296–302.

Rogers, L. (1997) New data-logging tools – new investigations. *School Science Review,* 79 (287): 61–68.

Rogers, L.T. & Wild, P. (1996) Data-logging: effects on practical science. *Journal of Computer Assisted Learning,* 12 (3):130–145.

Rowell, P.M. (1997) Learning in school science: the promises and practices of writing. *Studies in Science Education,* (30): 19–56.

Russell, T.J. & Harlen, W. (1990) *Assessing Science in the Primary Classroom: Practical Tasks.* London: Paul Chapman.

Sadler, R (1989) Formative assessment and the design of instructional systems. *Instructional Science,* 18:119–44.

Scaife, J. & Wellington, J. (1993) *Information Technology in Science and Technology Education*. Buckingham: Open University Press.

Scheerens, J. (1991) Process indicators of school functioning: a selection based on research literature on school effectiveness. *Studies in Educational Evaluation*, (17): 371–403.

Schilling, M., Hargreaves, L., Harlen, W. with Russell, T.J. (1990) *Assessing Science in the Primary Classroom: Written Tasks*. London: Paul Chapman.

Scottish Council for Research in Education (SCRE) (1995) *Taking a Closer Look at Science*. Edinburgh: SCRE.

Scottish Office Education and Industry Department (1998) *Assessment of Achievement Programme: Science 1996*. Edinburgh: SOEID.

Sensor! (1998) [Classroom materials]. Amersfoort, The Netherlands: Christelijk Pedagogisch Studiecentrum (CPS).

Shapiro, B. (1988) What children bring to light: towards understanding what the primary schools science learner is trying to do. In: P.J. Fensham (Ed) *Directions and Dilemmas in Science Education*. Brighton: Falmer Press.

Shapiro, B. (1998) Reading the furniture: the semiotic interpretations of science learning environments. In: Fraser, B. & Tobin, K. (Eds) *International Handbook of Science Education*, 609–622.

Shayer, M. & Adey, P. (1981) *Towards a Science of Science Teaching*. London: Heinemann Educational.

Shayer, M. & Adey, P. (1992a) Accelerating the development of formal thinking in high school students III: testing the permanency of effects. *Journal of Research in Science Teaching*, 29 (10): 1,101–15.

Shayer, M. & Adey, P. (1992b) Accelerating the development of formal thinking in middle and high school students II: post-project effects on science achievement. *Journal of Research in Science Teaching*, 29 (1): 81–92.

Shayer, M. & Adey, P. (1993) Accelerating the development of formal thinking in middle and high school students IV: three years on after a two year intervention. *Journal of Research in Science Teaching*, 30 (4): 351–66.

Shulman, L.S. (1987) Knowledge and teaching: foundations of the new reform. *Harvard Educational Review*, 7 (1):1–22.

Shulman, L.S. (1991) Pedagogical ways of knowing. In: Kam, H.W. (Ed) *Improving the Quality of the Teaching Profession. International Yearbook on Teacher Education, 1990.* Singapore: Institute of Education.

Smith, R. & Peacock, G. (1992) Tackling contradictions in teachers' understanding of gravity and air resistance. In: Newton, L. (Ed) *Primary Science: The Challenges of the 1990s.* Clevedon: Multilingual Matters.

Solomon, J. (1980) *Teaching Children in the Laboratory.* Croom Helm.

Solomon, J. & Simpson, M. (1989). Contribution as discussants. *Proceedings of the Conference on Adolescents' Thinking in Science.* Brighton: Falmer Press.

Solomon, J., Duvee, J., Scott, J. & McCarthy, S. (1992) Teaching about the nature of science through history: action research in the classroom. *Journal of Research in Science Teaching,* (29): 409–421.

Standing, L., Conezio, J. & Haber, R.N. (1970) Perception and memory for pictures: single trial learning of 2500 visual stimuli. *Psychonomic Science,* (19): 73–84.

Stiggins, R.J., Griswold, M.M. & Wikelund, K.R. (1989) Measuring thinking skills through classroom assessment. *Journal of Educational Measurement,* (26): 233–246.

Stofflett, R.T. (1994) The accommodation of science pedagogical knowledge: the application of conceptual change constructs to teacher education. *Journal of Research in Science Teaching,* 31 (8): 787–810.

Strike, K.A. & Posner, G.J. (1985) A conceptual change view of learning and understanding. In: West, L. & Pines, A. (Eds) *Cognitive Structure and Conceptual Change.* Academic Press.

Sugarman, N. & Mayer, R.E. (1988) Forward transfer of different reading strategies evoked by adjunct questions in science text. *Journal of Educational Psychology,* (79): 189–191.

Summers, M. & Kruger, C. (1992) Research into English teachers' understanding of the concept of energy. *Evaluation and Research in Education,* (6): 95–111.

Summers, M. & Kruger, C. (1993) *A longitudinal Study of Primary School Teachers' Understanding of Force and Energy. Working Paper 18: PSTS project.* Oxford University Department of Educational Studies and Westminster College Oxford.

Summers, M. & Mant, J. (1995a) A survey of some primary school teachers' understanding of the Earth's place in the universe. *Educational Research*, 37 (1): 3–19.

Summers, M. & Mant, J. (1995b) A misconceived view of subject-matter knowledge in primary science education: a response to Golby *et al* 'Some researchers' understanding of primary teaching. *Research Papers in Education*, 10 (3): 303–307.

Swain, J.R.L. (1996) The impact and effect of Key Stage 3 science tests. *School Science Review*, 78 (283): 79–90.

Swain, J.R.L. (1997) The impact and effect of Key Stage 3 science tests. *School Science Review*, 78 (284): 99–104.

Swain, P. (1997) The iodine clock reaction – a spreadsheet simulation to test. *School Science Review*, 79 (287): 81–86.

Taber, K.S. & Watts, M. (1996) Constructivism and concept learning in chemistry: perspectives from a case study. *Research in Education*, (58): 10–20.

Tamir, P. (1985) Consent analysis focusing on inquiry. *Journal of Curriculum Studies*, (17): 87–94.

Targan, D. (1987) A study of conceptual change in the content domain of the lunar phases. *Proceedings of the Second International Seminar on Misconceptions and Educational Strategies in Science and Mathematics*, (2): 499–511. Ithaca: Cornell University Press.

Tasker, C.R. (1981) Children's views and classroom experiences. *Australian Science Teachers' Journal*, 27 (3): 33–37.

Tobin, K. & Fraser, B.J. (Eds) (1987) *Exemplary Practice in Science and Mathematics Education*. Perth, Western Australia: Western Australia Institute of Technology.

Tobin, K. & Garnett, P. (1988) Exemplary practice in science classrooms. *Science Education*, 72 (2): 197–208.

Trumper, R. (1995) Students' motivational traits in science: a cross-age study. *British Educational Research Journal*, 21 (4): 505–515.

Vitale, M.R. & Romance, N.R. (1992) Using video-disc instruction in an elementary science methods course: remediating science knowledge deficiencies and facilitating science teaching attitudes. *Journal of Research in Science Teaching*, 29 (9): 915–928.

Vosniadou, S. (1997) On the development of the understanding of abstract ideas. In: Harnqvist, K. & Burgen, A. (Eds) *Growing up with Science*. London: Jessica Kingsley Publishers.

Wason, P. & Johnson-Laird, P. (1972) *Psychology of reasoning: structure and content*. London: Batsford.

Watts, M. & Bentley, D. (1987) Constructivism in the classroom: enabling conceptual change by words and deeds. *British Educational Research Journal*, 13 (2): 121–135.

Watts, M., Gould, G. & Alsop, S. (1997) Questions of understanding: categorising pupils' questions in science. *School Science Review*, 79 (286): 57–63.

Webb, P. (1992) Primary science teachers' understandings of electric current. *International Journal of Science Education*, (14): 423–429.

White, R.T. (1991) Episodes and the purpose and conduct of practical work. In: Woolnough, B.E. (Ed) *Practical Science*. Milton Keynes: Open University Press.

Williams, M.J.J. (1993) Biodiversity consortium (Teaching and learning technology projects). *The CTISS File*, 15, April, 50–51.

Woolnough, B.E. (1997) Motivating students or teaching pure science? *School Science Review*, 78 (283): 67–72.

Wragg, E.C., Bennett, S.N. & Carré, C.G. (1989) Primary Teachers and the National Curriculum, *Research Papers in Education*, 4 (3): 17–37.